Mickey Mouse Annuals left to right
1930 *(top left)* to 1940 *(centre bottom)* and 1942 *(bottom right)*

THE HAMER
COMIC ANNUAL GUIDE

Martin Hamer

Published by
Hamer 20th Century Books

Front cover by kind permission of DC Thomson and Co Ltd
Express Newspapers PLC
IPC Magazines
Back cover by kind permission of DC Thomson and Co Ltd
Grateful acknowledgement is made to the original artists

First published in UK in 2000 by Hamer 20th Century Books
Springfield Woodsetts Worksop S81 8QD England
Tel UK 01909 569428 International 00 44 1909 569428
Fax UK 01909 566900 International 00 44 1909 566900
Email enquiries@hamerbooks.co.uk
www.hamerbooks.co.uk

Conditions of sale

Printed and bound in Worksop UK by Bayliss Printing Ltd

ISBN 0 9537875 0 8

Contents

The Hamer Comic Annual Guide

This Guide to identifying and pricing collectable British annuals and comics has a special section on Rupert Bear.

What this Guide wishes to achieve

Our specialist book company Hamer 20th Century Books was established in 1986 and during that time we have had countless telephone calls asking us to identify or value a book for a customer. Several guides to identification and to a lesser extent valuation have been written but I believe this to be the most comprehensive guide to pricing British comics and annuals.

Listed you will find just about every significant annual published in the 20th Century. In most cases these would have been published for children though a few were intended for adults and I have also included a couple of the more collectable cartoonists. Where an annual has a specific relationship to a comic or story paper I have endeavoured to include its date and value too. The emphasis however is on the word Annual rather than the word Comic.

And what it doesn't

You will find very few references to annuals which were published exclusively in the 19th Century or to annuals which began their lives after 1979. Comics or story papers which did not have annual counterparts are largely ignored as are most annuals which did not run to a second issue.

Colour Plates and Images

All books for which cover images are provided in this Guide are from our own stock or from private collections. They represent books we have sold over the years. Obviously the copyright for the books themselves rests with the publishers – clearly identified and acknowledged in each case – and the artists. The photographs in this guide were all commissioned by Hamer 20th Century Books.

My grateful thanks go to:
DC Thomson and Co Ltd for permission to reproduce Dandy and Beano Annual and Comic covers,
Express Newspapers for permission to reproduce the Rupert Bear covers,
IPC Magazines for IPC Amalgamated Press and Fleetway covers, and Disney Enterprises Inc for the Mickey Mouse covers.

Condition

Good – for its age

An antique dealer friend of ours keeps a pebble in his pocket and when anyone tries to sell him something that they claim to be old he produces it with a flourish and says,
"That's old, probably millions of years old. How much are you going to give me for it?"
Age is not necessarily a good thing with comics and annuals either. The older they are the fewer people remember them. We are talking after all about nostalgia where the reader can return in an instant to their childhood. Nostalgia does not exist beyond living memory.

The most significant factor in determining the value of an annual is its condition and it simply won't do to say,
"It's old" or "It's good for its age."
Another remark we often hear is,
"It's not scribbled in."
I should hope not! The condition of a book is an absolute and the fact that a child owned it or it had been stored in a shed for 50 years is of no interest to the purchaser. The prices in this guide unless otherwise stated are for books in VERY GOOD condition.

It's Mint - inside

VERY GOOD (VG) means that the book is complete in every respect although it is clear that it has been read and handled and there are signs of minor wear to the edges and corners of the covers. The covers and especially the spine are what stare out at the collector from the shelf and unsightly bumps and tears will not be compensated for by pristine contents.

The name of a previous owner in the appropriate place does not prevent a book from being VG nor does the fact that it is price clipped but these two things are unacceptable to some collectors and may therefore impact on the value of the book. Many annuals have competition pages, dot-dot, colouring pages etc. If these are neatly completed the book may still be VG but if they are removed or untidily completed the value drops markedly.

FINE (F) is the next rung up the condition ladder. A Fine book will generally cause a flutter in the heart of the collector. The book shouts condition at you. Clearly it is not brand new but you would have to be really nit-picking to fault it. Fine books may still be price clipped or have the previous owner's name but they are more irritating in a Fine book than one in VG and you will find the price is significantly affected.

Top of the ladder is MINT (M). This simply means that a book is indistinguishable from new. No name, no price clip, no bumps and all corners and edges straight as a die. Sometimes you can even hear the book creak slightly on opening.

On the bottom rung of the condition ladder stands POOR (P). You would not normally entertain such a book unless it is terribly scarce. It may have the odd page missing, be warped with ancient damp or be nibbled by mice. But don't despair just yet. Look at the section on RESTORATION.

GOOD (G) although no match for his superior brethren VG, F and M looks down rather contemptuously on POOR. Books in GOOD condition may have covers which are quite worn or rubbed and at worst may lack an inch or so of spine.

Squeezed in between Poor and Good is READING COPY – sometimes flatteringly called Research Copy. This book has to have complete contents but may lack the whole spine and be pretty heavily worn but the collector just wants to read it.

So from top to bottom the conditions run Mint – Fine – Very Good – Good – Research/Poor.

Give or Take a Bit

Sometimes books don't quite make it from one grade to another and the plus scales are brought into play. Thus a book can be Near Fine or VG Plus. We never apply minus scales. A book described as Good Plus always seems to me to be more positive than one described as VG Minus.

Comics

Comics are usually divided into grade A, Grade B or put 'em in the bin. Grade A would be as for FINE or MINT and Grade B for GOOD or VERY GOOD.

Comics issued for Christmas, April Fool, Bonfire Night etc are known as specials and can be double the prices quoted in this Guide.

Collectors should be aware that dealers in American comics have incredibly precise definitions – tiny dividing lines between Good and Fine but massive distinctions in price. This guide deals only with comics issued in Great Britain.

Comics or Story Papers?

Story Papers are the earliest form of comics. Strictly speaking a publication without comic strips cannot be a comic. Papers like Gem and Magnet although illustrated did not carry comic strips so they were story papers. Gradually it dawned on publishers that boys and girls wanted less dense prose and the relief of pictures. I remember hardly ever reading the long stories. In fact I'd be interested to hear how many of you actually even read the prose under the Rupert Bear strips – the simple verse was enough for most of us. You couldn't call it laziness – we read for recreation for Pete's sake. The comics were our soap operas and they took us on to the more serious and examinable soap operas like Shakespeare's history plays.

Some publications were clearly story papers – Nelson Lee Library -

and some clearly comics – The Beano. But there is quite a bit of blurring at the edges. Adventure published by DC Thomson may have started as a paper but was very definitely a comic by the 1940's.

A Handful of Dust

The worst fault in a comic is when it browns and turns brittle. This happens when a comic is kept in conditions which are too hot and dry. And those hard plastic slip covers don't help. It's no good thinking well this title in Grade A is worth £100 so my brown, brittle job must be worth a tenner. It's worth nothing! It's disintegrating for Heaven's sake.

Slightly Foxed

The brown speckles which develop on some books and comics over time result from the printing process. If the foxing is only light then it detracts little from the price of Very Good or Fine items. If the foxing is dense then the devaluation is more dramatic.

What if my Book is Signed?

Comics and annuals unlike Modern First Editions rarely turn up signed by the author or artist. We have had a few Rupert Annuals for example that were signed by AE Bestall and these sold for about three times their normal unsigned price. Mary Tourtel's signature on a book is even scarcer although we did have one in auction - a rather poor Monster Rupert for 1933. I have never seen a Dandy, Beano or any other DC Thomson publication signed by Dudley Watkins for example but imagine such an item if it exists would go through the roof at auction.

Occasionally a book turns up with the extra bonus of a little original sketch. At a recent event some one was offering a 1975 Rupert Annual which not only had AE Bestall's signature but a pen and ink head of Rupert to boot. The book itself was worth about £10 but the asking price was £400.

Books signed by John Harrold are also much sought after by collectors. See the section on Rupert Bear.

Book Plates

Sometimes a book has the signature of the artist or author to a book plate which is stuck inside the front board. Some collectors tell us that they feel this is a rather inferior way to have a book signed as the artist hasn't actually touched the book. However it's better than no signature.

Dustwrappers

If a book was originally produced in a dustwrapper then strictly speaking it is incomplete without it. The most obvious example is the 1936 Rupert Annual which is worth £2000 in VG with a VG wrapper and £350 without the wrapper. Dustwrappers are graded in exactly the same way as books.

Restoration

Opinions as to whether to restore or not to restore will differ from collector to collector. Say you have a lovely book with a page missing and a friend who has a complete copy. Wouldn't it make sense to photocopy their page and have it professionally inserted in your book? Of course it would. The same would be true if you had a nice book sans spine – colour photocopies can be obtained quite cheaply - and a professional could restore your book to completeness although obviously if you were ever to sell the book you would have to draw the purchaser's attention to the restoration. Incidentally even if you are only photcopying a black and white page it is best to get a colour copy as this will look more authentically aged. You should always check out copyright restrictions before photocopying material.

Simply restoring a spine, restitching a book that is sprung or inserting the odd page or endpaper won't cost an arm and a leg. It is possible however to go to town and have your book intricately bound in embossed leather, having each page cleaned so the whole thing looks like new in which case prepare to write a four figure cheque.

Lay, Lady Lay

The restoration of dustwrappers is more controversial. Tiny repairs don't seem to worry anyone but sometimes the wrapper is so badly chipped, torn or holed as to require laying down. The entire wrapper is laid on to archive paper and the missing bits painted back in, leaving it possibly twice as thick as it was originally. Most people would be perfectly happy with their brightly restored book. Some would be less so. I know which I'd rather see on my shelf.

Who will buy my books and my comics?

Selling to the Trade

Comic and booksellers like anyone else have to pay their mortgages, their taxes, their overheads. We perform an important service to collectors and without dealers there would be nobody to coordinate collecting. So the labourer is worth his or her hire. It would be unrealistic therefore for anyone to expect to sell a VG 1954 Topper Book to a dealer for £80 as listed in this Guide. At Hamer 20th Century Books we would pay approximately £55 for such a book. That is really a very good deal for the price of a phone call – no stand rent, no overnight accommodation fees, no tax etc.

You will not endear yourself to a dealer if you telephone everyone in Yellow Pages and keep ringing back asking for an improved offer. The most likely outcome is that you will give everyone the hump and be left with your book unsold.

Comics like Goalkeepers are Different

So you've got 500 comics which according to this guide are worth £5 each. That's £2500. Call it £1600 to the trade.
Right?
Wrong!
Comics move extremely slowly and the dealers might have to wait years for a return on their investment. Your 500 comics are probably only worth about £500 to the trade.

Selling through Advertising to Collectors

Forget it! If you can find the right advertising medium you will get a grim response if you are unknown to collectors. They have learnt that buying from amateurs and part-time dabblers brings serious problems. Books and comics may turn up in unacceptable condition and they have hell's own job getting their money back. Most collectors prefer to deal with dealers whose reputations have been established over the years and who belong to associations like the Provincial Booksellers Fairs Association (PBFA).

Selling through Auction

Selling though specialist auctions is probably the best way of realising the potential of your books and comics. Even then it is most important that you are realistic in pitching your reserve – the sum under which you would not sell. The reserve should be at least one third below The Hamer Guide price – two thirds with comics. Although our own auctions at Hamer 20th Century are usually conducted at weekends and are well attended by collectors, this is not the rule and most auctions are attended only by the trade and in mid-week.

The main benefits of selling via auction are that someone else has the bother of cataloguing, storing and carting the stuff about and that commission of around 10% - 15% is all you pay.

Selling on the Net

Anything I say about the Internet will be out of date as soon as it's said. Although I have no doubt this is where the future lies for both collectors and sellers the medium is as yet fraught with difficulties. Even if you have your own Web Site the chances are nobody will find you unless you are well up the Search Engines' league tables. Professional booksellers with hundreds of books to sell are finding it worth their time to persevere through the technological swamp but it's hardly going to be viable to sell half a dozen titles.

The same issues apply as with selling any collectables. Can the buyer be sure the book is as described? Can they get their money back? Even when you are selling worldwide from a croft in Orkney or a loft in Cuckney you need the back-up of a professional reputation. There are now auction houses on the Net which allow you to build up a reputation via feedback from your customers but it is a painstaking process and not one to commit to just to empty the attic.

Collectors will always want to handle – even smell - the goods. Will this be possible by the time I've finished this sentence?

And where should I buy?

From a reputable specialist dealer who is a full member of the PBFA or similar organisation. Specialist dealers actually offer much better value than dealers with a more casual interest in a subject. They are used to handling hundreds of books in their specialism in the course of a year. They know what is genuinely rare and what is more common and are unlikely to overprice books. Such dealers also issue regular catalogues which allow you the luxury and comfort of buying from home and reigniting that old excitement of sending away for something like we did as kids. I waited with great longing for my Dan Dare Periscope.

Loyalty to a specialist dealer also brings its rewards as if you are in regular contact your name is most likely to spring to mind when that little gem turns up.

You will rarely hear a quibble from a professional dealer if you want to return or change a book for some good reason. You won't win friends though by returning a VG book because you bought it in the hope that it would turn out Fine.

We have all heard the car boot and jumble sale tales and it may still be possible to hit the odd bargain from an amateur dealer but if you seriously want to put a collection of books or comics together then you must approach it in a business like way. Decide what you want to collect, how much you can afford, how long you want it to take and get going.

Dating

Most annuals are known by the year after publication. Obviously this is a good ploy for the publishers as it extends the shelf life of the book. This is no doubt why a lot of annuals did not bear a date at all – no date and it never passes its sell-by. Rupert Bear Annuals are the great exception, always being known by the year in which they were published but they weren't dated until 1958. DC Thomson Annuals were dated from 1966 (Published 1965).

Some books are double-dated for the year of publication and the following year. Chums Annuals are an example.

Where books are undated I have produced brief descriptions of annual covers where known. Most books however are dated or at least numbered.

Your help

Undoubtedly there will be some errors and omissions in this Guide. I've yet to read a single guide that I didn't want to take issue with on some point or other. I plan to produce the next issue of the HAMER GUIDE in 2002 and would greatly appreciate the help of any reader in supplying information that you believe is missing or erroneous in this book. I will happily give a full acknowledgement to anyone providing authenticated information which will be helpful to readers of The Hamer Comic Annual Guide No 2.

The British Library

The British Library - 96 Euston Road London NW1 - houses most of the books mentioned in The Hamer Guide and you can do your own research although you will have to apply in person for a Reader Pass. You will also need to be reasonably computer literate to search their catalogue. Once you have found the book you are looking for it can be ordered for viewing at your desk although each order takes about an hour to process.

Comics are housed separately at the Newspaper Library, Collindale Avenue NW9.

Acknowledgements

We are not born with a comprehensive knowledge of books and comics. My own experience of buying and selling books and comics has been invaluable in putting this Guide together but I would like to acknowledge the assistance over many years of the late Messrs Leonard Matthews and George Turner.

I would also like to thank Gordon and Christine Bramham and June and Ian Pillinger for their help.

Martin Hamer

The word Annual is omitted from book titles

Adventure

They were all published by Wm Collins until 1936. The same title was published by TV Boardman in the 1950's and issued in dustwrappers.

1916 – 1936	£8 each
1953 – 1959	£ 10 each

Adventure Land

This book ran from 1923 to 1940 and was the Annual companion to Adventure Comic also published by D C Thomson. Originally 5/- and later 3/- the books have just about kept pace with inflation and are great value today at around £25 each.

1924 Island castaway tries to attract ship with smoke from fire
1925 Young man and German Shepherd in the mountains
1926 Young scout with palm tree background
1927 Young man, tent and rifle
1928 Trapper on skis with rifle
1929 Boy on bough above river
1930 Young man landing boat
1931 Bi-plane diving
1932 Three men and two husky dogs
1933 Two men on raft with red shirt as flag
1934 Man in canoe pursued by American Indian
1935 "Bill Jones First Up" placard held by boy hiker
1936 Boy and wolves in snowscene
1937 Man, racing car and tiger
1938 Man entering cave with pistol
1939 Man in loin cloth with sledgehammer
1940 Man with gun leading leopard
1941 Two men in canoe besieged by arrow assault

Adventure Comic Paper

Adventure was the first of The Big 5 DC Thomson publications – Hotspur, Rover, Wizard and Skipper followed – appealing to a broader audience than the boys' story papers thereto available. Dixon Hawk was the star detective attraction.

No 1 17th September 1921	£150
1921 – 1939	£8 each
1940 – 1949	£5 each
1950 – 1959	£3 each
1960 – 1961	£2 each

Subsumed by Rover
See Dixon Hawk

Adventures of Robin Hood

These books were a spin-off from the television series. They were published by Adprint and each one was numbered.

1956 – 1959	£8 each

See Robin Hood

Aircraft

1950 – 1975 (Ian Allen)	£6 each

All Stars Football Book

1962 – 1981 (World Distributors)	£5 each

Ally Sloper

Not only Britain's but the world's first comic strip cartoon character. He made his first appearance, the creation of Charles H Ross assisted by Mrs Ross (Marie Duval), in 1867 in the popular weekly Judy as half of the duo Sloper and Moses. He became the central character of his own comic Ally Sloper's Half Holiday in May 1884. Ally Sloper maintained a presence on the comic stage until 1977 being drawn by no lesser lights than Frank Hampson - better known for Dan Dare - and Frank Bellamy but nobody surpassed the drawing of WG Baxter who took Soper to his boozy limits.

All the following were published by WJ Sinkin until Gilbert Dalziel bought the rights from Ross and took over in 1884.

1880 – 1887 Ally Sloper's Summer Number	£30 each
1884 Ally Soper's Half Holiday	£40
1884 – 1887 Ally Sloper's Christmas Holidays	
(Illus WG Baxter)	£40 each
1888 – 1913 (Illus WF Thomas)	£40 each

Andy Capp

Andy Capp was Reg Smythe's creation for The Daily Mirror and made his bow in 1957. This disreputable beer swilling rogue and his long suffering wife Florrie were much loved by the public and over 50 books of the strips were issued. The first 17 were unnumbered although they were dated from No 6. They were usually published twice yearly.

No 1 1958 The Andy Capp Book   No 2 1959 Bottle shaped Spring Tonic
No 3 1959 Life With Andy Capp   No 4 1960 Andy C. Spring Collection
No 5 1960 The Best of Andy Capp   No 6 1961 Laugh with Andy Capp
No 7 The World of Andy Capp   No 8 More Andy Capp
No 9 Andy Capp – Must Be Dreaming No 10 Andy Capp Picks his Favourites
No 11 Happy Days With Andy Capp   No 12 Laugh at Life with Andy Capp
No 13 Andy Capp and Florrie   No 14 All the Best from Andy Capp
No 15 Andy Capp (Bathing)   No 16 Andy Capp (Carving initials)
No 17 Andy Capp (Scoring goal)

The first book is worth about £15 and you should be able to pick up the rest for about £5 each. Books after No 17 are quite common and worth a couple of quid each.

Andy Pandy

Those of us who could afford a telly watched Mary Adam's creation Watch with Mother from the early 1950's. Remember Looby Loo and Teddy?

1959 – 61 (Adprint)	£10 each
1962 – 1970 (Purnell)	£6 each
1970/80's (Purnell)	£5 each

See Robin Comic where Andy Pandy appeared on the cover from 1953. He also featured in Pippin in the 1970's.

Archie Andrews

Sunday dinner times will never be the same without Peter Brough, Beryl Reid, Max Bygraves and Archie of course. There's something wonderfully British about putting a ventriloquist act on the radio - A good idea – son!

1953 –1957 (Planned Bookselling) Dustwrappers	£20 each
1958 (New – Thames Publishing)	£15
1961 (Year Book - Swan)	£15

The 1950's Palitoy Doll comes complete with a Peter Brough mask and is worth £80.

Arthur Askey

A very much sought-after book ten years ago but not so much today, its success was due to the 1930's radio programme Band Wagon.

1940 (Oxford University Press)	£50

See Radio Fun

Avengers

Patrick MacNee and Diana Rigg first appeared on our TV screens as John Steed and Emma Peel in 1961. A whole collecting culture has developed around the series. The curious thing about the Avengers comic appearances is that they were published in rival publications from Fleetway and DC Thomson almost simultaneously.

1969 (Atlas)	£15
1975 –1978 (World Distributors)	£5 each

See Diana, June and TV Comic

Baby's

1916 (Frowde)	£15
1916 – 1937 (Dean)	£10 each
1930 – 1937 (Collins)	£10 each

Baby's Own

1933 – 1958 (Amalgamated Press)	£10 each
1959 – 1968 (Fleetway)	£5 each
1969 - 1980's (IPC)	£4 each

Batman

Batman (Bruce Wayne) with his side-kick Robin the Boy Wonder (Dick Grayson) seeks to purge the criminals from Gotham City especially his arch rival The Joker. The Annuals were published by Atlas until 1968. The double year dating system was employed until 1967.

1960/61	£60
1961/62 – 1967	£20 each
1968 (Top Sellers)	£10
1968 (Story Book – World Distributors)	£15
1970/80's (Various publishers)	£5 each

Batman Comic

Batman comics were first published in May 1939 in No 27 of Detective Comic jointly by DC Comics – no relation to the Scottish firm – and National Periodical Publications in the USA and early issues fetch astronomical sums. Their British counterparts were printed in black and white and published/distributed by Altas in the early 1950's. They are dated and numbered inside the front cover.

No 1	£120
Nos 2 – 5	£30 each
Nos 6 – 10	£20 each
1950/60's	£10 each

See Smash

Battler Britton

As well as in these two books Spitfire ace Battler appeared in many issues of Thriller Picture Library also published by Amalgamated Press. He began in No 160 in 1957 drawn by Colin Meritt. Expect to pay £7 -£10 each for them. He was also drawn by Geoff Campion for Sun comic from 1956.

1961 and 1962 (Amalgamated Press in dustwrappers)   £12 each

See Knock-out
See Thriller Picture Library
See Sun Comic

BBC Children's Hour/ Children's

1952 – 1960 (Burke Publishing)   £6 each

Beano, The

The Beano books and comics have been and still are a vital ingredient in British comic culture. Much of the Beano's success was down to the brilliance of artist Dudley D Watkins whose work for DC Thomson began as early as 1925. He drew Biffo the Bear for the Beano comic cover, taking over from Reg Carter's Big Eggo - who had made the page his own since the comic's beginning - in 1948. Watkins also drew Lord Snooty, Our Gang, The Shipwrecked Circus, Jack Flash, Jimmy and his Magic Patch, Strang the Terrible and Tom Thumb amongst others.

But Watkins was not on his own and the publishers boasted a whole host of talent. Most notably there were David Law (Dennis the Menace), Ken Reid (Jonah and Roger the Dodger), Leo Baxendale (Bash Street Kids) and Hugh McNeill (Pansy Potter).

The books and comics continue to thrive and are of course still published by DC Thomson.

Beano Book – See Colour Plates

We have sold an especially clean example of the first Beano Book for £3500 at our Auction in October 1996 and a slightly less than VG copy for £2350 in October 1999. In the same October 1999 Auction a bidder paid over £1000 for a VG 1941 and nearly £1700 for a VG/Fine 1942.

1940 No 1	£3000
1941	£1000
1942	£1000

In 1942 Magic Fun Book folded after two years and The Beano Book became the Magic-Beano Book.

See Magic Fun Book

Magic-Beano Book

1943	£700
1944 - 1946	£350
1947 - 1949	£250
1950	£150

Beano Book

1951	£100
1952 - 1953	£80
1954 - 1959	£70

Beano Books from the early 1960's in really Fine condition are scarce. The books were laminated from 1961 and a common fault is for the lamination to have cracks at the spine edge.

1960 - 1965	£60
1966 - 1969	£40

Beano Books from the 1970's have to be in Fine condition to command a price of £12 - £15

Beano Books from the 1980's and 1990's can be bought in Fine condition for around a fiver each.

Beano Comic

DC Thomson published No 3000 15th January 2000.

The comic was issued fortnightly between 1941 and 1949 because of paper shortages.

These days it is very difficult to establish a price for Beano No 1. In 1993 I bought a copy at Sothebys for around £700 and sold it for £1000. The very same comic changed hands a year later for in excess of £4000. In 1996 a lovely example in our October auction failed to make its reserve of £2500. And now one has just been knocked down at auction for over £6000 – it did have its original Whoopee Mask free gift, possibly the only one extant. So what the next one will make is debatable.

No 1 30th July 1938 (With Whoopee Mask)	£5500
No 1 30th July 1938 (Without Whoopee Mask)	£3000
Nos 2 – 5	£400 each
1938 – 1939	£100 each
1940	£70 each
1941 - 1945	£40 each
1946 – 1949	£20 each
1950 – 1959	£6 each
1960 – 1964 (Scarce years)	£8 each
Thereafter	£1 - 2 each

Expect to pay double for specials – Christmas, Bonfire Night, April Fool etc.

Beezer

Ferocious two year old Baby Crockett drawn by Bill Ritchie and Malcolm Judge's The Numbskulls were favourites of mine. All were published by DC Thomson.

1958 Characters climbing steep staircase	£100
1959 Human pyramid holding up title	£25
1960 Baby Crocket featured	£20
1961 Globe wearing cap	£15
1962 Characters inside train	£15

1963 Pirates peep through title	£15
1964 Commissionaire with title to hatband	£15
1965 Colonel Blink banging on drum	£15
1966 – 1969	£8 each
1970's	£5 each
1980's	£4 each

Beezer Comics

Dudley Watkins' loveable Ginger was the heart and soul of Beezer. The comic was published by DC Thomson as a tabloid until the 1980's when it assumed a smaller format.

No 1 21st January 1956	£120
Nos 2 – 10	£15 each
1956 – 1959	£6 each
1960's	£3 each
1970/80's	£1 each

Beryl the Peril

Beryl is the British institution to match her publishing house co-star Dennis the Menace and she was drawn by the same artist David Law. The annuals were published by DC Thomson in alternate years to Dennis. 1961 saw the first laminated cover as with Dandy and Beano.

1959 Beryl sawing her way through to matt front cover	£80
1961 Beryl drilling pneumatically in cowgirl gear –	£20
1963 Beryl sublimating on punch ball	£20
1965 Beryl leads tiger on a rope	£20

Beryl first appeared in Topper Comic No 1 on 7th February 1953.

See Topper

Best of All

1923 –1924 (Renwick)	£5 each

Beverly Hillbillies, The

These three books featured Granny (Irene Ryan), Elly Mae (Donna Douglas), Jethro (Max Baer) and Jed (Buddy Ebsen) from the wonderful TV series. They were all published in UK by World Distributors.

1965 – 1967   £10 each

Big (Budget) Book for Boys/Children/Girls

These books were edited by the Strangs. Herbert edited the boys' books and Mrs Strang looked after the children and the girls. See Herbert Strang for interesting revelations about the editors' identities. Richard Bird, CE Brock, Florence Harrison and Dorita Fairlie Bruce made significant contributions.

1927 – 1943 (Humphrey Milford/Oxford
   University Press)   £8 each

Big Enid Blyton Story

Enid Blyton was quite simply the most prolific children's writer of the century. She was born in 1897. When she was in her early teens her parents split up acrimoniously. The separation of parents was not to be spoken of at this time and Enid had to painfully pretend her father was away on business. She had a successful school career and worked as a governess all the time writing and sending her work off to publishers only to receive countless rejections. By the time she was 24 she began to have poems and stories published in magazines and her first anthology Child Whispers appeared in 1922.

She married Major Hugh Pollock in 1924 and had two daughters. Eighteen years later the marriage ended in divorce after Enid's apparent infidelity with K Darrell Waters whom she subsequently married. Enid Blyton died in 1968 after Alzheimer's Disease had taken slow hold.

She was a strong woman in the predominantly male publishing world and soon became used to getting her own way. She would keep a tight control over the way her books were produced and if she was not satisfied would either threaten to switch to another publisher –

she had over twenty - or actually do so. By 1950 she had her own copyright company. She was responsible for over a thousand books in her time as well as contributing to countless magazines and anthologies.

1962 (Odhams)	£15
1970/80's (Purnell)	£5 each

See Enid Blyton
See Noddy

Big Top Circus

1941 and 1942 (Amalgamated Press)	£15 each

Bill Boyd Western

1957 - 1961 (Miller)	£10 each

Bill Boyd Western Comic

1950 - 1955 (Miller)	£6 each

Billy and Bunny

The book ran from 1921 - 1949 with an eight year gap after 1941. Prices ranged from 2/6 to 4/- and they're probably priced about the same today at £15 each. They are scarce and rather lovely and so are the people who are interested in them. They were published by John Leng of Dundee.

1922 Pulling log through snow	1923 Dated Xmas 1922 on cover
1924 Castle steps, pixies/snowballs	1925 Broomsticks and snowman
1926 Giant Turkey	1927 Father Christmas held up
1928 Downhill sledging	1929 Circus ring
1930 Skiing	1931 Father Christmas at party
1932 Toy Train	1933 Sailing in a boat
1934 Huge reflections in mirror	1935 Billy jumps through hoop
1936 Punch and Judy Show	1937 Bagpipes and drum
1938 Learner drivers	1939 Smile please!
1940 Hot air balloon	1941 Riding tandem

There were three issues published in the late 1940's all of which we have had in stock but failed to keep a note of the covers. Your help would be appreciated if you have the details.

Billy Bunter's Own

Bunter the creation of Frank Richards – real name Charles Hamilton but also know as Martin Clifford, Owen Conquest and Hilda Richards – first appeared drawn by Charles Chapman in The Magnet which was published by Amalgamated Press from 1908 – 1940. The first issue is worth about £70 but there is also a facsimile worth about £10. Sad to say there has been a decline in the popularity of these papers in recent years and you can probably pick them up for a couple of quid each.

1953 Footballer Bunter (Mandeville) Dustwrapper	£15
1954 Sledging Bunter (Mandeville) Dustwrapper	£15
1955 Unseated Bunter (Mandeville) Dustwrapper	£15
1956 – 1960 (Oxenhoath) Laminated boards	£10 each
1967 (Holiday – Odhams)	£10

See Greyfriars Holiday Annual, Holiday Annual, Knock-out, Magnet and Valiant

Billy the Kid Western

1953 – 1961 (World Distributors)	£8 each
1958 and 1959 (Picture Stories – Amalgamated Press)	£8 each

Geoff Campion drew him for Amalgamated Press' Sun comic and Billy quickly established himself as a front page colour star.

1952 – 1959	£6 each

See Thriller Picture Library

Bimbo

Aimed at very young children, all were published by DC Thomson.

1963 Penguin Pip looks at mirror image in snowman	£8

1964 Cute chick and Pip play hoopla	£8
1965 - 1969	£5 each
1970/80's	£3 each

Bimbo Comic

Dudley Watkins drew Tom Thumb for this DC Thomson publication.

No 1 18th March 1961	£10
Other issues to 1972	£2 each

Black Bob

These books - there were so many gaps you can't call them annuals - are best identified by what appears on the back cover. There is a vibrant market in Black Bob and it is a definite area in which to invest. Black Bob and his master Andrew Glenn were the creation of Jack Prout and first appeared in The Dandy on November 25th 1944. All were DC Thomson publications.

1950	Shepherd approaches Bob up mountain	£100
1951	Bob and little boy survey sheep below them	£50
1953	Bob watches two birds on his bowl	£35
1955	Bob pulls girl and pup in tub	£35
1957	Shepherd pats Bob's head	£25
1959	Bob with three dogs	£25
1961	Front cover shows six frames of Bob	£30
1965	Back cover shows Bob with trophies	£20

See Dandy Comics and Annuals

Blackies Annuals for Boys and Girls/Boys/Boys' Stories/Children's/Children's Budget/Girls/ Girls' Stories/Little Ones

The books had contributions from no lesser lights than AE Bestall, Ruth Cobb and Marsh Lambert.

1904 - 1941 (Blackie and Son, London)	£10 each

Blue Peter

All were published by BBC Publications but the success of the first book was underestimated and it quickly became scarce. The mistake was not repeated and apart from No 2 the books are quite common.

1964 No 1	£100
1965	£30
1966 – 1969	£5 each
1970/80's	£3 each
No 18 has Rupert Bear content	£6

Bobby Bear

There are widely varying formats from the small card covered issues published first by the Daily Herald and then by Dean and Son until 1930 and then from 1931 in the large hardbacked form - actually known as 1932 thus leaving a gap. Original stories were by Kitsie Bridges with illustrations by Dora McLaren.

1920	£20
1922 – 1930	£12 each
1935 (Budget)	£8

It continued to be published from 1941 – 1969	£5 each

Bobsey Twins

All were published by World Distributors.

1957 – 1964	£6 each

Bonanza

All were published by World Distributors as a spin-off from the popular television series.

1963 – 1969	£10 each
1964 and 1968 (Book)	£10 each
1965 (Comic Album)	£10

Bonanza Comic

1963 – 1969 (World Distributors)	£6 each
1970's (Top Sellers)	£2 each

Bonny

All were published by Swan.

1950	£6
1952 – 1956	£5 each

Bonzo

Bonzo was the creation of GE Studdy and the lovable dog starred in many cartoon films in the 1920's. The annuals which were all published by Dean were preceded by many other books from 1922. Amongst the most valuable of these are the SW Partridge publications The Bonzo Book 1925, New Bonzo Book 1927 and Bonzooloo Book 1929 which are worth around £200 each. Look out too for little card covered books published by Thomas Allen in the 1920's and worth about £75 each. The annuals were undated and are described as follows:

1935 Bonzo Laughter Annual	£150
1936 Majestic Bonzo on throne	£120
1937 Bonzo in clown garb with balloon	£120
1938 Bonzo with skipping rope	£120
1947 Jack in the Box	£50
1948 Donkey and cart	£50
1949 Peashooter and fez	£50
1950 Parrot	£50
1951 Cowboy	£40
1952 Rocket Ship	£40

See Joy

Book of Soccer

All were published by Stanley Paul.

1946 – 1947	£8 each
1959 – 1969	£5 each
1970	£4 each

Bo-Peep

1883 – 1919 (Cassells)	£15 each
1921 – 1927 (Cassells)	£10 each
1928 (Nursery Story Book – Ward Lock)	£15
1928 – 1936 (Bumper Book – Amalgamated Press)	£10 each

See Chick's Own

Bookano Books

A wonderful series of pop-up books which were all published by Strand Publications. There are 19 to collect numbered 1 – 17 except for Bookano Stories (1936) and Bookano Zoo (1939) which bear no number.

1935 – 1950	£50 each

Boys

As you might expect there are many titles that begin with the word Boys. Check some of these out:

Adventure Book 1936, Book of All Sports 1950, Book of Bridges 1939/1941, Book of Cricket 1949 -1954, Book of Famous Liners/Railway Engines both 1950, Book of Flying 1938, 1939 and 1941, Book of Magic 1950, 1952 and 1957, Book of Popular Hobbies 1953 – 1956, Book of Space 1953 – 1956, Book of the Air 1954 – 1955, Book of Tunnels 1939 and 1941, Own Companion 1960 – 1963, World Annual 1964 – 1972

These books can be bought for a few pounds each and represent excellent value covering areas of great collectable interest such as Magic and Flying.

Boys and Girls Book/Book of the Year

See Daily Express Children's Annual

Boys' Cinema

They were mostly published by Amalgamated Press in dustwrappers.

1932	£45
1933 – 1941	£20 each
1947	£20
1949 – 1951 and 1953 (Boys and Girls Club – Juvenile)	£15 each

Boys' Cinema Paper

All were published by Amalgamated Press.

No 1 13th December 1919	£30
1919 – 1940	£5 each

Boys' Own

The bound copies of the boys' paper were first issued in 1879. There were copious colour plates and if any of these are missing values are seriously affected. Each volume is dated or numbered to the spine. They were published by Religious Tract Society until 1940. The society was founded by George Burder in 1799. I counted contributions from 8 reverends in the 1889/90 issue. Laugh? I thought I never would! Ah but there were contributions from Jules Verne, A Conan Doyle, GA Henty and illustrations by Randolph Caldecott and Louis Wain to compensate.

1879/80 Volume Nos 1/2	£80
1881/1882 Volume Nos 3/4	£65
1883 – 1940 Volumes 5 – 62	£35 each
1965 – 1976 (Boys' Own Annual for Boys - Purnell)	£5 each

Boys' Own Paper

There were three series published by Religious Tract Society until 1963 and then by Lutterworth.

No 1 18th January 1979	£30
1879 – 1911	£5 each
1911 – 1913	£5 each
1913 – 1967	£5 each

Brave Book for Boys/Children/Girls/Tinies

| 1940 –1942 (Oxford University Press) | £8 each |

British Boys/Girls

| 1912 – 1926 (Cassells) | £15 each |
| 1928 – 1934 (Amalgamated Press) | £10 each |

British Legion

Both were published by Dean.

| 1933 Circus Ring Cover | £15 |
| 1934 | £8 |

Bronco Layne

| 1959 and 1964 (World Distributors) | £10 each |

Broons, The

Dudley D Watkins joined the staff at DC Thomson of Dundee in 1925 at the age of 18. Ten years later he was given the responsibility by his boss Mr RD Low for drawing The Broons and Oor Wullie for a new supplement to the Sunday Post. The Broons family – Paw, Maw, Daphne, Hen, Horace, Joe, The Bairn, The Twins and Granpaw – from No 10 Glebe Street won immediate favour amongst the readership. In 1939 the first Broons book was published with Watkins also responsible for the cover work and title page which he signed Watty – quite an honour as DC Thomson artists rarely signed their work.

| 1940 | The Broons look out at reader with names below each | £3000 |
| 1942 | Maw and Paw with smaller family portraits around | £2000 |

1948	Paw reading newspaper, Maw serving tea	£1000
1950	The Broons family clustered and smiling out at reader	£500
1952	The Broons sitting at table looking out at reader	£350
1954	Family watch Maw and Paw dancing	£300
1956	The Broons looking out of window	£ 80
1958	The Broons playing various board games	£60
1960	Paw addresses The Broons at dinner on 25th January	£40
1962	The twins playing board game on floor, Paw shaving	£30
1966	Maw and Paw dance/Twins play mouth organs/Maggie piano	£30
1968	Dated	£25
1970's		£8 each
1980's and 1990's		£4 each

Brownies

1959 –1961 (Thames)	£5 each
1959 (Brownies Year – Wm Collins)	£5
1962 – 1968 (Purnell)	£5 each
1969 onwards into the 80's (Brownie – Purnell)	£3 each

Bruin Boys, The

The Bruin Boys Annuals were an important part of a whole strategy employed by Amalgamated Press to win the hearts of British children. The Bruin Boys Annual was aimed at younger boys. Tiger Tim was a central player in the strategy of course also appearing in Rainbow, Playbox and his own Tiger Tim's Annual. See also Mrs Hippo.

1927 – 1940	£20 each

Bubble and Squeek

1951 – 1954 (Birn Bros)	£5 each

Bubbles

1924 – 1925 (Bubbles Office/Fleetway House)	£12 each
1926 – 1943 (Amalgamated Press)	£10 each

Bubbles Comic

Vincent Daniel's The Children of the Forest was set in the merry camp of Robin Hood. The comic was aimed at very young children and was published by Amalgamated Press at Fleetway House.

No 1 16th April 1921	£30
1921 – 1941	£4 each

Subsumed by Chick's Own

Buck Jones

1957 and 1958 (Amalgamated Press)	£12 each

Buck Jones Comics

Buck Jones was drawn by several artists including Joseph Walker, Geoff Campion and Reg Bunn. His most famous comic appearances were in Cowboy Picture Library where he featured in No 1 6th May 1950 £50

See Cowboy Picture Library, Film Fun, and Comet

Budget for Boys/Children/Girls

1933 – 1941 (Nelson)	£5 each

Buffalo Bill Wild West

Available only through Woolworths in 1949, by issue No 4 it was on sale in every bookshop in Britain such was the demand for this wonderful book. Denis McLoughlin excelled with the colour artwork. Annuals for 1950 – 1961 were numbered 2 – 13.

1949 – 1954 (Published in dustwrappers – TV Boardman)	£25 each
1955 – 1957 (Popular)	£15 each

1958 – 1960 (Wild West dropped from title - Dean)   £15 each

Buffalo Bill Comics and Papers

The early papers were published by Aldine who were also
responsible for Robin Hood in the same format.

1899 – 1932 (Aldine)	£2 each
1948 – 1952 (TV Boardman)	£5 each
1955 – 1956 (Cody added to title – Miller)	£7 each

Bugs Bunny

1964 –1968 (World Distributors)	£10 each
1964 and 1965 (Comic Album)	£8 each
1970/80's	£4

Bumper Adventure/for Boys/for Boys and Girls/for Children/for Girls/for Little Folks

1925 – 1941 (Nelson)   £15 each

Bunty Book for Girls

These lovely books published in dustwrappers by DC Thomson are
terrific value at around a fiver each.

1960 Silent Night
1961 The Songs we Sing at Christmas
1962 Little Town of Bethlehem
1963 January and February
1964 Ballerinas
1965 Dated from here onwards

Bunty Comics

Bill Holroyd's The Four Marys and The Dancing Life of Moira Kent
by Ron Smith were among the most popular features. All were
published by DC Thomson.

No 1 18th January 1958   £10

1958 – 1968	£2 each
1970/80's	£1 each

Buster Book

Buster was the son of Andy Capp and was created like his father by Reg Smythe.

1962 – 1965 (Soft covers - Fleetway)	£10 each
1966 – 1969 (Fleetway)	£6 each
1970/80's (IPC Magazines)	£4 each

See Andy Capp

Buster Comic

This was initially a tabloid Fleetway production. It was the first weekly to be produced by Fleetway after they took over from Amalgamated Press.

No 1 28th May 1960	£40
Other issues to 1969	£4 each
1970/80's	£1 each

Incorporated Radio Fun (1961), Film Fun (1962) and Cor (1974)

Butlin's Beaver

1962 and 1963 (Fairhaven)	£6 each

Butterfly

1939 and 1940 (Amalgamated Press)	£18 each

Butterfly Comic

Portland Bill the creation of GM Payne featured on the comic's front page from 1907. He was an old lag looking for work. Ten years later his named was changed to that of the comic in which he had held sway for almost twenty years – Butterfly Bill.

No 1 17th September 1904	£40

All other issues including Firefly and Jolly to 1939   £5 each

Calling Nurse Abbott

1964 (World Distributors)   £10

Camberwick Green

1968 and 1969 (Purnell)   £12 each
1970's   £4 each

Candy and Andy

All were published by World Distributors.

1968   £5 each
1970/71   £4 each

Captain Marvel Comics

Unassuming Billy Batson yelled "Shazam!" and became Captain Marvel.

No 1 December 1944 (Miller/Fawcett)   £50
1945 Miller/Fawcett issue for Captain Marvel Jnr   £20
1946 – 1954 (Miller)   £12 each
1946 – 1954 (Captain Marvel Jnr – Miller)   £6 each

See Marvelman/Young Marvelman

Captain Scarlet

These annuals were spin-offs from the poular Gerry Anderson
television series Thunderbirds.

1967 (And the Mysterons Century 21)   £15
1968 (City Magazines)   £12
1969 (And Thunderbirds - City Magazines)   £10

Cassells for Boys and Girls/Children/Holiday

Florence Mary Anderson was the principal illustrator. There were
stories by Arthur Bryant and Marian Wood.

1910 –1933 (Cassells)   £15 each

Champion

1967 and 1968 (Fleetway)   £6 each

Champion for Boys

As with the girls' version the annual did not appear between 1941 and 1949 when War Economy Standards affected the availability of paper.

1924 - 1925 (Champion Office/Fleetway House)	£10 each
1926 – 1942 (Amalgamated Press)	£8 each
1932 – 1940 Champion Book for Boys (Dean)	£8 each
1950 – 1952 Champion Book for Boys (Dean)	£8 each
1947 – 1956 (Amalgamated Press No issues 1943 –1946)	£5 each

Champion Comic Paper

All were published by Amalgamated Press.

No 1 28th January 1922	£50
1922 – 1939	£5 each
1940 – 1949	£4 each
1950 – 1955	£2 each

Champion incorporated Triumph in 1940 and was itself subsumed into Tiger in 1955. Fleetway published a new version of Champion Comic which ran to 15 issues in 1966 before joining forces with Lion. These are worth about £2 each today.

Champion Book for Girls

The books were all published by Dean but there appear to have been no issues for 1941 – 1949.

1932 – 1952   £5 each

See Champion for Boys

Champion the Wonder Horse

1957 – 1962 (Daily Mirror)   £8 each

Charles Buchan's Soccer Gift Book

1957 – 1958 and 1969 (E Hulton and Co Ltd)   £5 each

Chatterbox

Individual Chatterbox papers were issued in weekly or monthly parts between 1886 and 1955 and they should cost you no more than £3 each today. Their publishers are reflected in the annuals as follows –

1863 – 1903 (Wells, Gardner and Darton)	£15 each
1904 – 1925 (Gardner and Darton)	£10 each
1915 – 1927 (Chatterbox Newsbox Wells, Gardner and Darton)	£10 each
1926 – 1930 (Gardner,Wells and Simpkin)	£10 each
1931 – 1933 (Simpkin/Simpkin)	£15 each
1934 (Chatterbox Co)	£15
1935 (Simpkin/Simpkin)	£15
1936 – 1951 (Dean probably no issues 1941 – 1944)	£10 each

Cherry Ames

1960 - 1964 (World Distributors)   £5 each

Cheyenne

1961 (Adventure Stories Adprint)	£10
1962 and 1964 (World Distributors)	£8 each
1963 and 1964 (Comic Album - World Distributors)	£8 each

Chickabiddies

1930 –1933 (Little Dots)   £8 each

Chicks Own

This book was aimed at very young children and claimed to be able to teach them to read – a surefire winner for frustrated parents no doubt. The device that Chick's Own came up with as the key to unlock the door that educationalists have sought to open since the first doodlings on cave walls was the hyphen. Apparently if you hyphenated ev-e-ry jol-ly syl-la –ble kids could just learn it au-to-ma-tic-al-ly. At least the poor souls had Stri-pey the Ti-ger and Ru-pert the Chick to compensate.

1924 – 1928 (Chicks Own Offices/Fleetway House)	£20 each
1929 – 1939 (Amalgamated Press)	£15 each
1940 – 1957 (Chicks Annual - Amalgamated Press)	£10 each

Chicks Own Comic

No 1 5th September 1920	£80
Other issues to 1957	£3 each

Incorporated Bo-Peep (1934) and Bubbles (1931) until itself being subsumed into Playhour in 1957

Children's Gift Book/Golden Treasury/Treasury

1932 – 52 (Various publishers)	£5 each

Children's

1870 – 1872 (Book Society)	£15 each
1916 - 1936 (Wm Collins)	£12 each
1921 (E Hulton and Co Ltd of Manchester) See Joy Book	
1934 – 1935 (Hutchinson)	£10 each

Children's Friend

This was another magazine to run for over a century (1824 – 1930) published in monthly parts by a variety of companies. SW Partridge bound the published parts into annuals from 1914

1914 – 1930	£15 each

Children's Holiday Fun

All were published by DC Thomson.

1937 Animals laugh at Mr Bunny stuck in deckchair   £15
1938 Characters rush right to left across busy
    beach scene   £15
1939 Characters rush left to right across beach   £15
1940 Zoo scene   £15

Children's Hour

See Uncle Mac

Children's Prize/Prize for Boys and Girls

The books were variously published by Dean, Wells, Gardner and
Darton, Chatterbox Office and Simpkin.

1863 –1934   £10 each

Child's Companion/Empire

These were bound copies of the monthly magazine.

1824 –1913 (Religious Tract Society)   £10 each

Child's Own

A slim, cheerful little book which survived for more than a century.

1834 – 1937 (Sunday School Union)   £10 each

Chips

Tramps Weary Willie and Tired Tim appeared on the front of all
three annuals.

1939 – 1941 (Amalgamated Press)   £10 each

Chips Comic (Illustrated Chips)

Albert Pease's Alfie the Air Tramp began life in the Joker which
joined forces with Illustrated Chips on 25th May 1940 and so did
Alfie. Both comics were published by Amalgamated Press.

No 1 26th July 1890	£30
No 1 (New Series) 6th September 1890	£30
All other issues to September 1953	£3 each

Took over Joker in 1940 and was subsumed into Film Fun in 1953

Chummy Book

Dorothy Russell contributed stories and illustrators included Chloe Preston and Frank Hart.

| 1914 – 1932 (Nelson) | £8 each |
| 1933 – 1942 (Nelson added to title) | £8 each |

Chums

The paper's best known author was Samuel Walkley who wrote serials from 1892 until 1940 and the best known illustrator was Thomas Henry who eventually drew Richmal Crompton's William. The handover between publishers probably caused some confusion over dating. They are all bound volumes. They appeared in dustwrappers from 1927/28 and you can expect to pay double the prices quoted.

1892/93 – 1926/27 but dated 1926 to spine	
(Vol 1 –33 Cassells)	£30 each
1927/28 - 1941 (Vol 34 – 48 Amalgamated Press)	£25 each

Chums Papers

See bound volumes above for publishers.

| No 1 14th September 1892 | £50 |
| Other issues to 1932 | £5 each |

Subsumed into Modern Boy

Circus Boy

| 1958 – 1960 (Purnell) | £12 each |

Cisco Kid

1954 - 1956 (World Distributors)   £15 each

Cisco Kid Comic

1952 – 1955 (World Distributors)   £7 each

Classics Illustrated

Not strictly within the compass of The Hamer Guide as there were no annual counterparts. However Classics Illustrated (Classic Comics for the first 34 titles) made such an important contribution to British comic culture and were so instrumental in introducing children to classic literature that they cannot be passed by.

I won't attempt to deal with the US publications which began in 1941.

In Britain the comics were published/distributed by Thorpe and Porter between 1951 and 1963 although the dates are often difficult to determine as the comics were not issued in numerical order. They were also printed and reprinted sometimes with completely different covers. The dating of the edition in your hand is determined by a complicated factor known to collectors as HRN (Highest Reorder Number). This in its crudest form means that the higher the number printed in the list of available titles on the back of the comic the later the printing. If you have comic No 85 Dr Jekyll and Mr Hyde and the HRN is 150 then you will have one of the copious reprintings of that title.

Often the comic collector in this sphere is competing with collectors from the fields of Sherlock Holmes (None of the three Holmes titles was reprinted in UK and you could pay £100 each for the US editions), James Bond, Alice in Wonderland, Robin Hood and Mary Shelley (Frankenstein was not reprinted in UK and the US edition is £300 plus today) and this has pushed prices for some titles to a premium.

Mick Anglo from Marvel became British editor in the 1960's and drew some issues himself including Oscar Wilde's The Canterville

Ghost which sells today at £100.

Classics Illustrated 1951 - 1/3 issue price	£8 each
Classics Illustrated 1952 – issued at 1/-	£8 each
Classics Illustrated 1952 – issued at 1/6 Super de Luxe	£8 each
Giant Classics 1952 – issued at 2/-	£12 each
Classics Illustrated 1953 – 1963 – issued at 1/3	£8 each

Especially collectable titles
Dr No (Number 158a)	£300
Great Expectations (Number135)	£60
Alice in Wonderland (Number 49)	£50

Come on Steve

1948 and 1950 (Collins)	£8 each

Comicolour

1947 – 1955 (Swan)	£5 each

Commander Story for Boys

1957 (Sampson Low)	£5 each
1958 (Book)	£5 each
1959 – 1960 (Story and book dropped)	£5 each

Coronet

1957 (Story for Girls - Sampson Low)	£5
1958 (Book for Girls)	£5
1959 (Girls)	£5
1960 (Girls' Stories)	£5

Cowboy Book for Boys

1939 (DC Thomson)	£25

Cowboy Comics Album

1956 – 1959 (World Distributors)	£12 each

Cowboy Comic (Cowboy Picture Library)

These pocket-sized comics were published by Amalgamated Press/ Fleetway from 1950 to 1962 and ran to 468 issues.

Buck Jones appeared in No 1 The Fighting Sheriff drawn by Geoff Campion and shared appearances principally with Kit Carson who starred in No 2 as King of the West drawn by Derek Eyles and Eric Parker. Davy Crockett, Tim Holt and Kansas Kid also held sway some weeks. Early numbers are scarce.

No 1 6th May 1950 issued at 7d	£50
Nos 2 – 10	£20 each
Nos 11 – 50	£10 each
Nos 51 – 99	£8 each
Nos 100 – 463	£6 each

See also Film Fun where Buck Jones first appeared in 1933. He also featured in Sun Comic and Comet in the late 40's and early 50's and such issues are worth about £5 each.

See Buck Jones
See Kit Carson

Cowboy Hero Comic Album

1958 – 1961 (Miller)	£15 each

Crackerjack Book

1958 – 1962 (Daily Mirror)	£5 each
1967 (BBC)	£8
1969 and 1976 (Book of Games)	£10
1970's (Various publishers)	£4 each

Crackers

Alex Akerblath was responsible for most of the covers. The books also featured the artwork of Reg Parlett and Roy Wilson.

1933 –1941 (Amalgamated Press)	£8 each

Crackers Comic

JL Jukes' Ali Oop transferred from Jester on 9th March 1940 for issue No 2000 of this Amalgamated Press publication.

No 1 22nd February 1929   £30
Other issues to 1941   £5 each

Took over Sparkler in 1939 and was subsumed into Jingles May 1941

Crusoe

1926 (Newnes)   £25

Cubs and Brownies

1928 – 1931 (Wm Collins)   £5 each

Cub Scout

1969 – 1970 (Newnes)   £4 each
1970's (Odhams/ World Distributors)   £4 each

Curly Wee

1949 (Birmingham Mail)   £15

Cute Fun

1947 – 1956 (Swan)   £5 each

Daily Express Children's

All were published by Daily Express.

1930 – 1934 See Rupert Bear Section
1935 (Living Models) See Rupert Bear Section
1936 –1939 (Book of the Year/Book)   £25 each
1940 (Circa) Adventure Book with football game to centre £15

Daily Mail

All were published by Associated News mostly in dustwrappers.

1947 - 1955 (For Boys and Girls)	£8 each
1956 - 1962 (Boys/Girls)	£5 each
1958 - 1962 (Adventure)	£5 each
1962 (For Girls/For Boys)	£5 each
1963 (New Girls/New Boys)	£5 each
1964 - 1966 (Girls/Boys)	£5 each
1963 - 1967 (Jolly Jingles)	£5 each
1934 - 1941 (Nipper)	£12 each

Daily Sketch

All were Associated News publications in dustwrappers.

1957 - 1964 (Children's)	£5 each
1959 - 1961 (Modern Boys/Girls)	£5 each

Daily Worker Children's

1955 (Daily Worker)	£15

Dakotas, The

1962 (Purnell)	£10

Daktari

1967 and 1968 (World Distributors)	£10 each

Dalek

1964 (Book - Souvenir Press)	£60
1965 (Outer Space Book - Souvenir Press)	£60
1966 (World - Souvenir)	£60
1970's (World Distributors)	£5 each

Dan Dare

1953 Pilot of the Future Pop-up	£40

1953 and 1957 (Space Book)   £40 each
1963 (Space Annual)   £40

These books turn up but they are usually very well worn – hence the
VG prices. Also of interest is the 1950's Dan Dare Ingersol pocket
watch at £300 in VG condition.

Dandy, The - See Colour Plates

Dandy books and comics represented a sea-change in the
publisher's concept of what children wanted to read and all credit
to DC Thompson for recognising that change. Amalgamated Press
were quick to appreciate the success of their rival's ventures with
both Dandy and Beano and rushed similar format comics Radio Fun
and Knock-out into production.

Dudley Watkins was again the brightest star in the Dandy
firmament with Desperate Dan who appeared from 1937 until 1984
before making it full time on to the front cover. James Crichton's
Korky the Cat had held the cover spot - with only one week's
interruption from Allan Morley's Keyhole Kate in 1943 – for the
best part of fifty years. Danny Longlegs was another Watkins'
contribution. Bill Holroyd drew Plum MacDuff and Screwy Driver
whilst Jack Prout was responsible for Black Bob and Allan Morley
for Hungry Horace and Julius Sneezer.

Dandy Monster Comic

1939	£2500	1940	£1000
1941	£700	1942	£700
1943	£450	1944	£450
1945	£350	1946	£350
1947	£350	1948	£250
1949	£250	1950	£150
1951	£100	1952	£60

Dandy Book

DC Thomson began laminating their annuals from 1961 and the
issues to 1969 are difficult to find without cracks in the lamination
especially around the edge of the spine.

1953 – 1960	£45
1961 – 1965 (Difficult to find without lamination breaks)	£65
1966 – 1969	£30
1970's	£8
1980's and 1990's	£4

Dandy Comic

The comics were published fortnightly between 1941 and 1949 because of paper shortages. They appeared in alternate weeks with The Beano.

No 1 (With Free Gift)	£3500
No 1 (Without Free Gift)	£2500
No 2	£600
Nos 3 – 10	£300 each
Issues from 1938	£80 each
Issues 1939 – 1940	£60 each
1941 – 1943	£50 each
1944 – 1947	£25 each
1948 – 1949	£20 each
1950 – 1955	£10 each
1956 – 1959	£5 each
1960 – 1964	£10 each
1965 – 1969	£3 each
1970's	£1 each
1980's and 1990's	£1 each

Dangerman

Patrick McGoohan first played Nato Secret Service Agent John Drake in the ITV production of 1961.

1962 (TV Crimebuster Series by TV Productions)	£15
1964 (Atlas)	£12
1965 and 1966 (World Distributors)	£12 each

Dangerman Comic

TV Adventure Comic No 231 1961 First Appearance	£15
Dangerman Comic (Thorpe and Porter)	£10 each

Deans

All were published by Dean as you might expect.

1937 (For Children)	£30
1957 (For Girls)	£5
1958 (For Boys)	£5

Denis Law's Book of Soccer

1967 – 1972 (Pelham)	£5 each

Dennis Compton

1951 (Mandeville)	£10
1952 – 1956 (Paul)	£8 each
1957 (Evans)	£8

Dennis the Menace

Dennis is a British institution although foremost a Scottish institution, published by DC Thomson. He first appeared - the work of David Law - on 17th March 1951 in a rather minor berth in the Beano Comic. Two years later he was promoted to the whole of Page 2 and less than a year after that was catapulted on to the back page in full colour. Actually Dennis had already appeared fleetingly on the front cover of The Beano in the Bumper Sports Issue of 1951 but it was not until 14th September 1974 that Biffo the Bear was finally ousted in Dennis's favour. And Dennis has been there ever since. The significant early books alternated annually with Beryl the Peril.

1956 No 1 Dennis marches along bearing a tin of paint	£120
1958 Dennis endangers all on his buggy	£60
1960 Dennis tries diving	£35
1962 Large papermache Dennis head above his own	£30
1964 Dennis bursts on to front page circus style	£30
1966 and 1968	£25 each
1970's	£15 each
1980's and 1990's	£4 each

Desperate Dan

Cow Pie gourmet Dan appeared in the very first issue of The Dandy 4th December 1937. It is greatly to the credit of original creator Dudley Watkins who drew Dan into the 1960's that this character endures today. In fact Dan was promoted to the front page of the Dandy 47 years after his creation. Strangely there was only one early annual dedicated to Desperate Dan and that was published in 1953 as a thin large format book with red, black and white strips. The book when it turns up today is often in rather worn condition. A VG example would set you back about £140. The next book was not until 1979 – worth about £8. Thereafter the books are worth about £4 each.

Diana

The Avengers appeared from 1967 in these DC Thomson publications. Nice dustwrappers can enhance the value markedly.

1966	£8
1967 – 1979	£4 each
1980's	£3 each

Dick Barton

Dick Barton was a favourite radio programme for many people who followed the adventures of this Secret Agent from 1946 to 1951. The books are difficult to find in VG dustwrappers so you could pay double listed prices.

1950 and 1954 (London Contact)	£10 each
1979 (Brown and Watson)	£5

See Comet

Diddymen

Ken Dodd's Diddymen as well as having their own annual appeared in TV Comic at the end of the 1960's.

1969 and 1970 (Argus)	£8 each

1970's (World Distributors) £4 each

Dingbats

1950 and 1951 (Shaw) £8 each

Dixon Hawk's Case Book

1938 – 1953 (There were two in 1939 - DC Thomson) £18 each

Dixon Hawk Papers

All were published by DC Thomson.

Library No 1 14th July 1919	£20
Other issues to 1941	£3 each
Casebook No 1 28th November 1938	£30
Other issues to 1953	£5 each

See Adventure Comic

Doctor Kildare

1964 (World Distributors) £15

Doctor Who

All were published by World Distributors.

1965 This book was remaindered and is fairly common in UK	£12
1966 – 1971	£40 each
1970/80's	£6 each

Donald Duck

All 5 books were published by William Collins.

1938
Front and back covers show Donald Duck in sailor uniform walking through a field inhabited by a bull. He holds a horse shoe in one hand and a pair of boxing gloves in the other. The covers bear the legend There's a Lot in it! The pictorial spine has a dazed and

plastered Donald. There is a coloured frontispiece.   £300

1939
Both covers show Donald Duck in sailor uniform driving a home-made car with a washboard radiator and boxing glove headlights. The Winner hangs from a drawing pin. The pictorial spine has Donald diving head first with detached steering wheel as the car gets the better of him. There is a coloured frontispiece.   £300

The British Library only has these two examples although I believe the remaining three annuals were dated from 1940 – 1943 and were priced between 3/- and 4/-   £250 each

Eagle

All are numbered and/or dated and Nos 2 – 11 had dustwrappers. The debate goes on as to whether No 1 had a dustwrapper but to the best of my knowledge one has yet to materialise. The original publishers E Hulton and Co were taken over by Longacre Press in 1960.

No 1 (E Hulton)	£45
Nos 2 – 11 in dustwrappers	£18 each
Nos 2 – 11 without dustwrappers	£8 each
Nos 12 – 18 (Longacre)	£6 each
1970/80's	£4 each
Eagle Sports Nos 1 – 8	£8 each
Eagle Sports 1961 – 1963	£5 each

Eagle Books

A good many titles were issued most of them in dustwrappers. These were not annuals of course but I list a few of the more collectable titles.

Book of Balsa Models 1953 and 1957	£15 each
Book of Magic 1956	£20
The Happy Warrior 1958 Comic strip biography of Sir Winston	£40
Book of Model Aircraft 1960	£20
Book of Model Boats 1962	£20

Book of Model Cars 1962	£20
Book of Police and Detection 1961	£20
Book of Rockets and Space Travel 1961	£20
Book of Spacecraft Models 1961	£20

Eagle Comic

Eagle was the brain-child of Rev Marcus Morris who was unhappy about what he regarded as an unsavoury trend to violence in imported American material. He was probably wrong of course because if heroes like Batman and Superman were to shine they needed the foil of disreputable foes.

Marcus Morris in his quest to elevate the moral tone of British comic culture had the good fortune to befriend art student Frank Hampson. At first they worked together on Morris' parish magazine which they hoped would go national. It was not long before they came to the realisation that a more direct route to the heart of the populace was needed – indeed a comic.

Hampson drew four strips for a mock-up of the first issue and the greatest of these was Dan Dare. Several publishers turned the tabloid comic down flat – Amalgamated Press for one – but Hulton Press had the good sense to take it on. The comic looked a giant amongst its rivals in austere early 1950 - sweets were just about still on ration – and the Eagle was an immediate success.

These comics are usually sold in Volumes although it is of course possible to buy individual issues. The very first issue 14th April 1950 was printed in good quantities – some say a million - and we believe was given away in some areas of the country as a promotion. Its large format however made it difficult to keep. The best way to manage a collection these days is to have them bound in volumes so they can be stored on shelves.

Issue No 1	£250
Nos 2 – 10	£20 each
Nos 11 – 50	£8 each

Thereafter the comics usually sell at around £2 – £3 each but you should expect to pay about £100 for complete Volumes which have 51 or 52 comics in each – Volume 4 had only 38 issues because of moving from an April starting date to January for Volume 5. Christmas issues and other specials may be twice as dear.

See Lion

Elvis Special

All were published by World Distributors.

1963 – 1969	£12 each
1970's	£5 each

Emergency Ward Ten Girls

1962 and 1963 (Purnell)	£8 each

See TV Picture Stories

Empire for Boys/for Girls

There were 25 Volumes for each sex.

1909 – 1933 (Religious Tract Society)	£15 each

Enid Blyton's

1947 – 1959 (Holiday Book - Sampson Low)	£20 each
1955 – 1958 (Magazine - Evans Bros)	£15 each
1958 (Annual - Olbourne Press)	£15
1965 (Bedtime - World Distributors)	£10
1960 – 1971 (Holiday Book - Sampson Low)	£8 each

See Big Enid Blyton
See Noddy
See Sunny Stories

Every Boy's

1927 – 1937 (Hobby - Amalgamated Press)	£10 each

1944 (Adventure - Wm Collins)	£10
1948 (Juvenile Productions)	£10
1949 - 1953 (Book of Sport - Clarke and Corkoran)	£5 each
1954 and 1955 (Book of Sport - Guildford Press)	£5

Every Girl's

1924 - 1929 (United Press)	£10 each
1939 (Adventure Nelson)	£12
1948 (Juvenile Productions)	£10

Express for Boys

| 1957 - 1960 (Daily Express/Oldbourne) | £8 each |

FA Book for Boys

Earlier issues had dustwrappers but they add nothing to the value.

| 1950 - 1969 (Heinemann) | £5 each |
| 1957/58 (Football Association Book for Boys - Naldret) | £5 |

Fabulous 208

| 1969 (Fleetway) | £8 |
| 1970/80's (From 1978 Fab 208 IPC) | £4 each |

Fairies Album

| 1945 - 1957 (Swan) | £6 each |

Fairy Folks

| 1926 - 1928 (Wm Collins) | £20 each |

Father Tuck's

These delightful books were published by Raphael Tuck and Sons Ltd. Several issues had illustrations by Janet Murray and Louis Wain. Editions with pop-ups are at least double quoted prices.

| 1899 - 1935 | £35 each |

Feathers

All were published by Featherstone Press.

1943 (Bumper)	£10
1944 (For Boys and Girls)	£10
1946	£10
1948 (Playtime)	£10

Felix

Felix the animated cat was the creation of Otto Messmer. He was such a success with the American public in the late 1920's that Walt Disney found it difficult to interest financial backers in Mickey Mouse.

1923 – 1930 (Daily Graphic and Daily Sketch)	£120 each
1956 (World Distributors)	£50
1961 (London) and 1962 (Purnell)	£40 each

See Modern Boy and TV Comic

Film Fun

They were published by Amalgamated Press until Fleetway in 1961. Laurel and Hardy featured on the cover of the first annual and most of the others.

1938 No 1	£150
1939	£90
1940	£80
1941 – 1945	£50 each
1946 – 1949	£30 each
1950 – 1959	£15 each
1960	£10
1961	£20

Film Fun Comic - See Colour Plates

The first issue included a photograph of Fatty Arbuckle as a free gift. Published by Amalgamated Press/Fleetway until 1961. Laurel and

Hardy, drawn by Bill Wakefield who set the standard for the comic, first appeared in No 563 on 1st November 1930 and stayed until 1957. The comic duo were later drawn by Bill's son Terry. Cowboy Buck Jones made a famous entry in 1933, Popeye a belated appearance in 1959 and Lucky Luke rode in on Jolly Jumper in 1960. The comic never attempted colour until flirting with a bit of red ink in its last days.

No 1 17th January 1920	£400
Nos 2 – 10	£25 each
Other issues to 1930	£8 each
1st November 1930	£25
Issues to 1940	£6 each
Issues to 1950	£5 each
Added Thrills to title on 13th June 1959 With Scoop Donovan	£10
Issues to 1962 (Tony Hancock issues worth double)	£ 4 each

Two comics of similar format and appearance - Film Picture Stories and Kinema Comic quickly folded and joined forces with Film Fun in 1932 and today are worth about £20 each.

Film Fun took over Chips in 1953
Subsumed into Buster in 1962 along with Radio Fun

Film Pictorial

1934 – 1940 (Amalgamated Press)	£30 each

Film Review

These fairly common books in the UK were usually in dustwrappers over plain boards. Cover appearances of James Dean, Marilyn Monroe and Elvis can double prices.

1945 – 1966 (Macdonald)	£15 each
Late 60/70's (WH Allen)	£10 each

Film Show

1964 and 1965 (Purnell)	£10 each

Fireball XL5

This was a Gerry Anderson spin-off from Thunderbirds.

1963 – 1966 (Wm Collins)   £10 each

Flash Gordon

Flash Gordon - polo player and astronaut - was the creation of Alex Raymond.

1968 (World Distributors)   £8
1970's (Brown and Watson)   £3 each

See Modern Wonder
See TV Comic

Flintstones

1963, 1964 and 1968 (Hanna-Barbera - World Distributors) £12 each
1963 (Flicker Fun - World Distributors)   £12
1964 and 1965 (Comic Album - World Distributors)   £12 each
1969 (Hanna-Barbera - Atlas)   £8
1970's   £4 each

Flip the Frog

Ub Iwerks, Disney's top animator left him in 1929 to work for Pat Powers where he invented the film cartoon character Flip the Frog. A single issue was published by Dean in 1931. It imitated the Mickey Mouse Annuals in style and content even to the point of having a coloured frontispiece and three additional colour plates £450

Flying Doctor

1964 (Dean)   £10

Football Champions

1964 – 1969 (Purnell)   £4 each
1970/80's   £3 each

Freddie Mill's Boxing for Boys

1954 – 1956 (Dakers)   £8 each

Fun Book for Boys

Both were published by DC Thomson with Dudley Watkins' covers.

1938 Four frames of two schoolboys in top hats   £60
1939 Elephant in dog kennel, large mouse chasing man   £60

Funnies

1944 – 1957 (Swan)   £6 each

Funny Wonder

The 1938 edition has a magnificent colour frontispiece of Charlie Chaplin drawn and signed by Reg Parlett.

1935 – 1941 (Amalgamated Press)   £15 each

Funny Wonder Comic

Amalgamated Press didn't get a bigger catch than Charlie Chaplin and he was drawn by Bertie Brown for the front page on 7th August 1915 – beware the facsimile is quite common – before being relegated to inside pages some 900 issues later and disappearing from the comic altogether in May 1944. Also worth a mention is George Parlett's Little Elf who ran for 6 years from May 1936. 19th Century editions exist – ironically it began as Wonder in 1892 whence it returned.

No 1 26th December 1914   £40
No 72 (Chaplin No 1)   £20
Other issues to 1942   £5 each

Incorporated Jester from 1940 and became Wonder once again in 1942
Wonder joined Radio Fun in 1953

Gamages Children's

1929 - 1931 (Gamages)   £10 each

Gem Paper

This boys' paper must be mentioned because of the importance of its contribution to British comic culture. Its days are numbered if not over in terms of its collectability but it ran for nearly 2000 issues from its beginnings on 16th March 1907. Charles Hamilton alias Frank Richards had created the school St Jims for Amalgamated Press' Pluck in 1906 and a year later placed Tom Merry into that worthy institution for the same publisher's Gem readers.

Gem papers today sell for between £2 and £5 although No 1 could be £50.

See Tom Merry
See Greyfriars Holiday
See Billy Bunter

Gene Autry

1950 (Rodeo Comic - Cartoon Art Productions)   £18
1955 - 1958 (Stories - Adprint)   £10 each

George Best's Soccer

1969 - 1973 (Pelham)   £5 each

Giles

The Giles Annuals were numbered to title page as First Series, Second Series etc. The first book was published in 1946 but covered cartoons from 1943. All originals were published by The Daily Express/Express Newspapers. All facsimiles are published by Pedigree Books.

Giles No 1   £200
Giles No 1 Facsimile in Green slipcase Mint   £40
Giles No 1 Facsimile in Grey slipcase as cover Mint   £30

Giles No 2	£225
Giles No 2 Facsimile in slipcase Mint	£30
Giles No 3	£175
Giles No 3 Facsimile in slipcase Mint	£30
Giles No 4	£175
Giles No 4 Facsimile in slipcase Mint	£30
Giles No 5	£175
Giles No 5 Facsimile in slipcase Mint	£20
Giles No 6	£65
Giles No 6 Facsimile in slipcase Mint	£20
Giles No 7	£65
Giles No 8	£20
Giles No 9	£15
Giles No 10	£15
Giles Nos 11 - 19	£10 each
Giles thereafter have little serious commercial value	£3 - £5

Girl

A sister publication to Eagle. When I'd finished reading Tiger I used to follow the adventures of the dizzy Lettice Leefe in my sister's Girl. They are all dated and can be picked up cheaply. Dustwrappers to 1961 roughly double quoted prices.

1953 No 1 (Hulton Press) in dustwrapper	£20
1953 without dustwrapper	£10
1954 – 1960 (Hulton Press)	£8 each
1958 – 1960 (Film and Television - Hulton Press)	£10 each
1961 - 65 (Longacre)	£8 each
1961 – 1965 (Film and Television - Longacre)	£10 each

Girl Books

Spin off titles from the annuals include from 1953 – 1959 Book of Hobbies/Modern Adventures/Outdoors/Ponies/World of Ballet
£8 each

Girl Comic

All were published by Hulton Press until 1960 when taken over by Longacre and eventually IPC until subsumed by Princess in October

©Express Newspapers PLC.

Early Rupert Annuals left to right
1936 *(top left)* to 1940 *(bottom left)*

Rupert Annuals left to right
1941 *(top left)* **to** 1949 *(bottom right)*

Rupert Annuals left to right
1950 *(top left)* to 1957 *(bottom right)*

©Express Newspapers.

A Collection of Scarce Rupert Titles

Left to right

Rupert at the Seaside (1952), Rupert Edward and the Circus (1949),
Little Bear and the Fairy Child (1922), Monster Rupert (1931), Rupert Music Book No 2 (1959),
Adventures of Rupert Little Lost Bear (1921), Rupert and the Snowman (1950), Rupert Again (1940),
Rupert Little Bear's Adventures No 1 (1924) and Monster Rupert (1934)

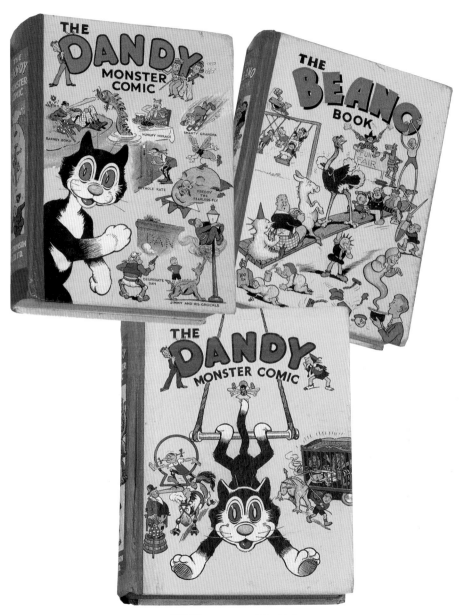

©DC Thomson and Co. Ltd.

Left to Right
Dandy Monster Comic No 1 1939, Beano Book No 1 1940
and Dandy Monster Comic No 2 1940

©DC Thomson and Co. Ltd.

Beano Books left to right
1941 *(top left)* to 1949 *(bottom right)*

1964. See Colour Plates

No 1 (2nd November 1951)	£40
Nos 2 – 10	£10 each
Thereafter	£2 each

Girl from U N C L E

United Network Command for Law Enforcement. In 1966 Napoleon Solo and Illya Kuryakin were at the mercy of their captors in The Moonglow Affair when who should come to the rescue but April Dancer, the Girl from Uncle? She was first played by Mary Anne Mobley (Miss America) and then by Stephanie Powers.

1967 - 1969 (World Distributors)   £8 each

Girl From U N C L E Comics

1967 (Gold Key)   £8 each

Girl Guides

1959 – 1961 (Thames Publishing)	£5 each
1962 – 1963 (Purnell)	£5 each
1964 – 1969 (The Girl Guide - Purnell)	£5 each
1970/80's	£3 each

Girls

1913 and 1914 (Budget of Short Stories - Nelson)	£12
1915 (Nelson)	£15
1915 (Library - Nelson)	£15
1935 and 1936 Hutchinson)	£10 each
1930 and 1931 (Adventure - Wm Collins)	£10 each
1939 – 1941 (Budget - Blackie)	£10 each
1941 – 1964 (Missing late 40's early 50's - Wm Collins)	£6 each

Girls' Crystal

We see the rare appearance of women illustrators like Evelyn Flinders and V Gaskell but the stories were almost exclusively written by men. However school mistress Vera Desmond BA was before her time.

1940 (Amalgamated Press)	£25
1941 – 1959 (Amalgamated Press)	£8 each
1960 –1969 (Fleetway)	£5 each
1970's (IPC)	£3 each

Girls' Crystal Comic

All were published by Amalgamated Press/Fleetway. See Colour Plates

No 1 26th October 1935 (The Crystal)	£60
Nos 2 – 9 (The Crystal)	£10 each
Issues 1936 – 1963	£3 each

Took over Schoolgirl in 1940

Girls' Empire

1902 - 1904 (Melrose)	£10 each

Girls' Fun

1948 (Fun Book Swan)	£8
1949 (Fun Special Swan)	£8
1950 –1957 (Swan)	£6 each

Girls' Own

A weekly paper for girls first published in 1880 by The Religious Tract Society. A few years ago we sold for a fiver each some issues to a museum preparing an exhibition on Victorian childhood. The Victoria and Albert Museum had put them in touch with us having refused to lend them their own few issues as they were too precious. What is their commercial value today? Still a fiver each. Girls' papers are terrifically good value. Mind you if you really start looking for them you probably won't find any.

Artists included Marcella Walker and Sydney Cowell but reproductions and engravings extended to the work of W Holman

Hunt and Florence A Saltmer.

The papers were bound into volumes and published as annuals between 1880 and 1941. A variety of bindings was employed from simple cloth to cloth gilt and even half morocco. If any of the colour plates are missing values drop markedly.

1880 – 1908 (Summer)	£30 each
1908 (Autumn) – 1941 (Papers issued monthly and bound yearly)	£30 each
1935 – 1941 (Containing EJ Oxenham or WE Johns Stories)	£50 each

Girls' Realm

All were published by Hutchinson.

1901 – 1915	£15 each

Girls' World

All were published by Odhams.

1966 – 1969	£5 each
1970/80's	£3 each

Golden

1925 (For Girls – Fleetway House)	£15 each
1926 – 1939 (For Girls - Amalgamated Press)	£10 each
1938 (Book of Stories - DC Thomson)	£25
1929 – 1938 (Budget for Boys/Girls - Blackie)	£15 each

Golden Comic

Roy Wilson contributed Lieutenant Daring and Jolly Roger who had made their debuts in Sparkler, another Amalgamated Press publication.

No 1 23rd October 1937	£35
Other issues to 18th May 1940	£5 each

Subsumed into Jingles

Granpop

Lawson Woods (1878 – 1957) was the creator of Granpop. He illustrated the Bow-Wow Book published by Nisbit in 1912 which is now worth about £100. Warne published the Mr and Mrs Books first in the large approx 8" x 8" (£40 each today) and then in the smaller boxed version between 1916 and 1920 (£20 per unboxed booklet).

1935 (Dean)	£60
1943 (Book Of Fun - Birn Bros)	£60
1946 (Popular - Birn Bros)	£40
1951 (Dean)	£30

Great Book

All were published by Oxford University Press.

1926 – 1932 (For Boys/Girls/Children/Tinies)	£12 each

Green Hornet

1968 (World Distributors)	£8

Green's Nursery

1948 and 1949 (Darton and Clark)	£15 each

Greyfriars Holiday

All were published by Amalgamated Press. The series began as The Holiday Annual for Boys and Girls. Frank Richards (Charles Hamilton – See Billy Bunter) practically wrote the books single-handed. He was about the only man who could have given Enid Blyton a run for her money.

1920	£35
1921 –1941	£25 each

See Holiday

Guinness Book of Records

Although a bestseller on publication the book's quickly-outdated, oddball information has not been hugely sought after by collectors. Edited by twins Ross and Norris McWhirter, a complicated publishing system saw the first book reprinted 4 times between October 1955 and January 1956 each time in green boards occasionally with a film wrapper. Thereafter the book was published more or less annually into the 1990's apart from two issues in 1956 and 1969 and no issues in 1957, 1959 and 1963.

All issues   £8 each

Gunsmoke

All were published by World Distributors.

1963 and 1964 (Comic Album)	£10 each
1964 and 66	£8 each
1970's	£4 each

Happy Girls' Book

A few years ago we had a lovely couple of examples. We were amazed to discover they only made the prices estimated here. They are surely a bargain as listed. All were published by DC Thomson.

1930 Girl in headband smiling at reader	£15
1931 Girl and small white dog	£15
1932 Girl and Parrot	£15
1933 Girl sitting on a stile	£15
1934 Girl with tent in background	£15
1935 Girl on weighing machine at station with friends	£15
1936 Girls playing hockey	£15

Happy Hours

1949 - 1951 (Pickering and Inglis)   £10 each

Harold Hare's Own Book

These books were published by Fleetway and have lovely laminated covers. They ought to be worth a lot more.

1960 – 1964   £8 each

Harold Hare's Own Paper

All were published by Fleetway.

No 1 14th November 1959   £20
All other issues   £2 each

The comic had the additional title of And Walt Disney's Weekly from April 1961 and was eventually subsumed into Playhour in April 1964.

Harper's Young People

Worth a mention although strictly outside the remit of The Hamer Guide, they were published by Sampson Low, Marston, Searle and Rivington with 12 colour plates between 1885 and 1890
                                                    £30 each

Also published in weekly parts   £8 each
Monthly parts with single coloured plate   £8 each

Herbert Strang's

These wonderful tomes were published by Frowde, Hodder and Stoughton and then by Hodder and Stoughton. Early issues had stories by Lillian Quiller-Couch and illustrations by Arch Webb. Before you start imagining good old Mr and Mrs Strang in their grey-haired dotage pouring out the benefit of their wisdom to British children you should appreciate that Herbert Strang was actually two blokes G. Herbert Ely and James L'Estrange. Oh yes, and so was Mrs Strang.

1910 – 1927 (For Boys)   £12 each

See Oxford for Boys

Hobbies

1932 – 1939 (Newnes)   £10 each

Holiday

1920 (For Boys and Girls - Amalgamated Press)   £35

See Greyfriars

Holiday Stories

1936 – 1941 (DC Thomson)   £20 each

Hollywood Album

1954 – 1961 (Sampson Low) In dustwrappers   £8 each

Hopalong Cassidy

1954 – 1959 (Stories Adprint)   £10 each
1960 - 1961 (Western Comic Miller)   £15 each

Hornet Comic

No 1 14th December 1963 (DC Thomson)   £15

See Hotspur

Hotspur Book for Boys

The robot Iron Teacher would probably have been able to handle
The National Curriculum these days. Then again probably not. All
were published by DC Thomson.

1935 Boys taught from blackboard in open air
   by The Big Stiff   £20
1936 Teacher conducting experiment before
   three Inuit boys   £20
1937 Teacher and boys on desert island   £20
1938 Boys armed with cricket bats rally to
   their teacher's aid   £20

1939 Teacher held hostage in cave/mortar
   board with threat   £20

1940 Schoolboy on motorbike No 26	£20
1941 Teacher frightened by tiger	£20
1943 Teacher and boys spring cleaning	£20
1949 The Iron Teacher in tank	£20

Although the comic continued to be published the annual did not reappear until 1966 and it was dated from then on.

1960/70's	£5 each
1980's	£3 each

Hotspur Comic Paper

This was another long-lived success story from publishers DC Thomson. Red Circle stories were undoubtedly the most popular feature – school stories always seemed to be. See Colour Plates

No 1 2nd September 1933 (Black Mask Free Gift)	£250
No 1 (Without Free Gift)	£150
No 2 (Jumping Frog Free Gift)	£100
1933 – 1939	£8 each
1940 – 1949	£5 each
1950 – 1959	£4 each
New Hotspur No 1 24th October 1959	£10
1959 – 1969	£2 each
Ran to 1981	£1 each

Subsumed Hornet in 1976

Huckleberry Hound

All were published by World Distributors.

1962 (And Yogi Bear)	£10
1962 – 1965 (Comic Annual)	£10 each
1964	£10
1967 – 1969	£8 each

Huckleberry Hound Weekly

All were published by City Magazines.

No 1 7th October 1961	£10
Issues to 1967	£4 each

Added Yogi Bear from 1964

Hulton's

All were published by E Hulton and Co Ltd.

1924 – 1937 (Girls' Stories)	£6 each
1926 – 1937 (Adventure Stories)	£6 each
1958 (Television/Hulton Press)	£6

Hurricane

1965 – 1969 (Fleetway)	£8 each
1970's (IPC)	£5 each

I Spy

The little 6d books sell today for around £4 each although certain titles are more sought-after such as I Spy Cars. The 1/- books with colour plates are worth about £6 each.

1955 – 1957 (News Chronicle)	£8 each

Ideal

All were published by Dean.

1932 – 1940 (For Boys/Girls)	£8 each
1936 (For Children/Tinies)	£8 each

Infant

The magazine was edited by Ethel Lindsay from around 1905. Authors included Florence Moore and Olive Chandler. Illustrators included AL Bowley, Felix Leigh and Harry Neilson.

1853 – 1914 (Magazine - Partridge)   £15 each
1932 – 1934 (Partridge)   £12 each
1935 and 1936 (Dean)   £12 each

International Football Book for Boys

All were published by Souvenir Press.

1960 – 1969   £4 each
1970's   £3 each

ITV

I have only ever seen the issue for 1963 published by TV Publications.

1963   £12

Jack and Jill

1939 (Pearson)   £20
1952 (All Colour Gift Book - News of the World) £6
1955 – 1959 (Amalgamated Press)   £6 each
1960 – 1969 (Fleetway)   £5 each
1970/80's (IPC)   £3 each

Jack and Jill Comics

These lovely comics came from the Amalgamated Press/Fleetway and ultimately IPC stable.

No 1 27th February 1954   £15
All other issues   £2 each

The comic had a voracious appetite for takeovers and variously acquired Playbox in 1955, Candy in 1970, Teddy Bear in 1973 and Toby in 1978.

James Bond

A highly recommended series to collect. You could pick them up for £10 each a couple of years ago.

1966 - 1968 (World Distributors)   £50 each

See Classics Illustrated

Jane

Jane was the creation of Norman Pett in The Daily Mirror and eight compilations appeared between 1944 and 1960 plus one in 1975 and one in 1982. The first eight are worth about £20 each and the other two £5 each. Original artwork is much sought after.

Japhet and Happy

All books listed were published by News Chronicle. The Daily News had published reprints from the newspaper from 1920 – 1929 worth £20 each.

1930 (On Arkub Island)	£15
1931 (Book)	£15
1933 – 1953 (Annual)	£12 each
1936 – 1940 (Holiday Book)	f.12 each

Jester

1936 – 1940 (Amalgamated Press)   £10 each

Jester Comic

Reg Parlett drew Larry the Larky Legionnaire from 1932 to 1939. Allan Morley better known as a DC Thomson artist drawing the likes of Hungry Horace and Keyhole Kate had started out as an Amalgamated Press employee on Funny Wonder and Jester. The comic was published from 23rd February 1924.

No 1	£40
All other issues	£5 each

In May 1940 the comic was subsumed into Funny Wonder.

Jingles

1936 – 1941 (Amalgamated Press)   £10 each

Jingles Comic

Strongheart the Wonder Dog of the Woods, the creation of GW Backhouse, had a five year run in Jingles from 1949 having previously featured in other Amalgamated Press publications Comic Life, Sparkler and Crackers.

No 1 13th January 1934	£20
All other issues to May 1954	£4 each

Took over Golden in 1940 and Crackers in 1941 before surrendering itself to TV Fun in 1954

Joe 90

Joe was the adopted son of Professor Ian McClaine and made an excellent contribution to the Cold War for a nine year old.

1969 (TV Publications)	£5
1970's (Argus)	£3 each

Joe 90 Comic

All were published by Century 21.

No1 18th January 1969	£30
33 issues 1968 – 1969	£8 each

Subsumed by TV21

John Wayne Adventure

1954 – 1959 (World Distributors)	£8 each

John Wayne Adventure Comic

The comics were also published by World Distributors.

No 1 August 1952	£20
Nos 2 – 82 (1958)	£8 each

Jolly Book

And there's a jolly lot of them!

1910 – 1916 and 1918 (Nelson)	£15 each
1917 and 1920 (For Boys and Girls - Nelson)	£15 each
1921 – 1927 (Nelson)	£15 each
1929 – 1933 (For Boys/Girls - Nelson)	£15 each
1934 – 1942 (Nelson's Book for Boys/Girls)	£12 each

Jolly Comic

Roy Wilson drew Jack Sprat and Tubby Hotpot for the front cover of the first issue . All were published by Amalgamated Press.

No1 19th January 1935	£20
Nos 2 – 250 (1939)	£4 each

Subsumed by Comic Cuts

Jolly Jack's

1935 – 1941 (Wm Collins)	£10 each

Jolly Jack's Weekly

The paper featured as a supplement in Associated News' Sunday Despatch.

No 1 20th August 1933	£20
Nos 2 – 70 (1934)	£4 each

Jolly Jinks

Both were published by DC Thomson.

1937 Party games	£15
1938 Circus theme	£15

Jolly Stories

1932 – 1936 (For Boys/Girls - Wm Collins)	£10 each

Joy Book Children's (Story Pictures for Little Folk)

These books are a treasure trove of embryonic and blossoming artwork. In the 1922 edition alone GE Studdy supplied the frontispiece and illustrated the first story. We find Flo Lancaster's Oojah illustrated by Thomas Maybank and the Adventures of Patrick Persian copiously illustrated by Louis Wain. Hilda Cowham also wrote and illustrated for the series. There was even a character called Mickey Mouse! With all this talent it's no wonder they had to wait until 1923 to introduce Mabel Lucie Attwell when she illustrated Fay Inchfawn's story The Fairy Mender. Incidentally George Studdy was responsible for the 1923 cover which has a wonderful early Bonzo – he was only named in 1922 - as part of the cast.

1921 – 1925 (E Hulton and Co of Manchester)	£30 each
1926 – 1933 A thicker edition published by Allied Newspapers	£15 each

Joy Street

The annuals contained contributions from Hilaire Belloc, GK Chesterton, Walter de la Mare and AA Milne.

1923 – 1936 (Blackwell)	£30 each

Judy Book for Girls

All were published by DC Thomson in dustwrappers.

1966 – 1969	£6 each
1970/80's	£3 each

Judy Comic

Bobby Dazzler attended a boys' school where her mother was matron. All were published by DC Thomson.

No 1 16th January 1960	£8
Nos 2 – 500 (Took over Emma in 1979)	£2 each

June

1962 – 1969 (Fleetway)	£6 each
1970/80's (IPC)	£3 each

June Comic

Cliff Richard had one and so did Lucky – a living doll.

No 1 18th March 1961 (Fleetway)	£8
Nos 2 – 690 (Fleetway/IPC) (Took over School Friend in 1965)	£2 each

Kenneth Wolstenholme's World Soccer

All were published by World Distributors.

1964 and 1968	£6 each
1970's	£3 each

Kiddies

1919 – 1927 (JA Sharp)	£10 each
1934 – 1936 (Box of Books - DC Thomson)	£15 each
1937 and 1938 (Playtime - DC Thomson)	£15 each

Kiddyfun

1944 – 1956 (Swan)	£6 each

Kiddyfun Comic

There were only 12 issues from 1945 – 1951 when it joined Girls Fun which was also published by Swan   £5 each

Kinema Comic

See Film Fun

Kit Carson

1955 – 1960 (Amalgamated Press)	£12 each

See Buck Jones.
See Cowboy Picture Library

Knock-out

Frank Richard's (actually Charles Hamilton's) creation Billy Bunter was quick as lightning for once. He must have known that he would be homeless when the Magnet had folded in 1940. He switched to a strip in Amalgamated Press's Knock-out Comic in 1939 and featured in all the annuals which were called Knock-out Fun Book until 1956. It is very difficult indeed to find books from the 1940's in acceptable condition. The annoying hyphen in the title eventually disappeared.

1941	£70
1942 – 1945	£50 each
1946 – 1949	£20 each
1950 – 1959	£8 each
1960's (Fleetway)	£8 each
1970/80's (IPC)	£3 each

See Billy Bunter, Greyfriars' Holiday, Holiday

Knock-out Comic

Amalgamated Press who had dominated the comic world in the 1920's (Magnet and Gem) had lost the initiative to DC Thomson in the late 1930's (Dandy and Beano) and Knock-out and Radio Fun were their armoury in the fight-back. One Billy Bunter – now revitalised – was a weighty part of their ammunition. The comic became known as Billy Bunter's Knockout from 1961.

Ali Barber drawn by Frank Minnnitt had a short life but a merry one 1939 – 1940 before turning up in the Sun in 1951 also published by Amalgamated Press/Fleetway.

No 1 4th March 1939	£300
Issues 1939 – 1940 (Incorporating The Magnet June 1940)	£30 each
Issues 1941 – 1949	£10 each
Issues 1950 – 1963 (Incorporating Comic Cuts September 1953)	£3 each

Lady Penelope

Lady Penelope was the glamorous side-kick to convict-turned-chauffeur Parker in the popular television series Thunderbirds.

1966 (City Magazines)	£10
1967 – 1969 (Century 21)	£8 each

Lady Penelope Comic

There were 122 issues published by City Magazines.

No 1 22nd January 1966	£30
Nos 2 – 122	£6 each

Laramie

1962 – 1964 (Purnell)	£8 each
1965 and 1966 (Dean)	£8 each

Lenny the Lion

1960 – 1965 (Daily Mirror)	£8 each

Lion

These marvellous books are greatly underpriced.

1954 – 1959 (Amalgamated Press)	£10 each
1960 – 1969 (Fleetway)	£8 each
1970/80's (IPC)	£4 each

Lion Comic

Barry Nelson drew Sandy Dean for this Amalgamated Press publication from issue No 1. The bullies of Tollgate School got something to think about over the next four years I can tell you. See Colour Plates

No 1 23rd February 1952 (Sports Stars in Action Free Gift)	£80
Nos 2 – 10	£10 each

All other issues to 1974   £3 - £5

Added The Sun in 1959, Champion in 1966 and Eagle in 1969 before
capitulating to Valiant in May 1974

Little Dots

All were published by Religious Tract Society except for 1940
which was published by Lutterworth who soon got fed up with it.

1887 – 1940   £12 each

See Playways

Little Folks

1834 – 1915 (Religious Tract Society)	£12 each
1930 – 1933 (Amalgamated Press)	£10 each
1958 – 1968 (Wm Collins)	£5 each
1969 (Playbook - Wm Collins)	£5

Little People's

1899 – 1931 (Raphael Tuck)	£30 each
1939 – 1941 (Play Book - Blackie)	£15 each
1939 and 1950 (Toy Book - Blackie)	£12 each

See Father Tuck

Locospotters

1957 – 1969 (Ian Allen)	£6 each
1970's	£4 each

Lone Ranger

Clayton Moore played The Lone Ranger for the American ABC
Network from 1949 to 1957. He was known as Kemo Sabe to his
Indian companion Tonto (Jay Silverheels) and rode into every
episode on Silver - a fiery horse with the speed of light – to
Rossini's William Tell Overture. The actor died in December 1999
aged 85.

1955 – 1968 (World Distributors)   £8 each
1958 – 1960 (Adventure Stories - Adprint)   £8 each
1958 – 1961 (Comic Annual - World Distributors)   £10 each
1970's   £4 each

Lone Ranger Comic

These were World Distributors publications reprinted by Dell for the UK.

No 1 1st January 1953   £15
Nos 2 – 66   £5 each
The comic reappeared briefly in the 1970's   £2 each

Lone Star

1956 – 1967 (Atlas)   £4 each

Lone Star Comic

British reprints were distributed by Atlas in the UK from 1952 to 1963 and were numbered but not always dated   £6 - £10

Look and Learn

1963 (For Boys - Fleetway)   £5
1964 – 1969 (Fleetway)   £5 each
1970/80's (IPC)   £3 each

There were a great many spin off titles none of which has achieved serious status in the collecting world. The encyclopaedic nature of the book probably militated against this as the information is too old to be of use and too recent to be of interest to researchers.

Look and Learn Comics

A nightmare to store loose but they do turn up in their original binders and are worth about £25 per 100 issues. They ran for 20 years from 1962.

Louis Wain

Louis Wain studied at the West London School of Art from 1877 – 1880 having decided against a career in music. At the age of 24 he married Emily Richardson who was ten years his elder and she sadly died only three years later.

He was of course most famous for his illustrations of cats and his big breakthrough came with the publication of A Kitten's Christmas Party – a drawing of some 150 cats - in Madame Tabby's Establishment published by MacMillan in 1886.

His career flourished and he contributed illustrations to The Strand, Illustrated London News and Boys' Own among many but he never made any money. In 1907 he was sued for debt and having lost the case sailed off to the USA where he worked for two years.

On his return after his mother's death he continued to produce at a prolific rate – the famous Cat Alphabet in 1914 was one significant project – but his financial situation continued to deteriorate and the Great War signalled a shortage of work for him.

His behaviour became increasingly bizarre and in 1924 he was certified insane eventually ending up in Bethlehem Royal Hospital (Bedlam) as a pauper. Attempts were made to rescue him from his plight; the Prime Minister even being involved at one time. He died still incarcerated in 1939.

Several of the annuals were issued in soft covers.

1901 and 1902 (Anthony Treherne)	£250 each
1903 (Comic Annuals ABC – Wm Collins)	£250
1903 (Hutchinson)	£250
1905 (King)	£200
1906 (Shaw)	£200
1907 and 1908 (Bemrose)	£200 each
1909 and 1910 (Allen)	£180 each
1911 – 1915 (Shaw)	£180 each
1921 (Hutchinson)	£180

Lucie Attwell, (Mabel Lucie Attwell)

Mabel Lucie Attwell was born into a large family in the East End of London in 1879. Her father was a prosperous butcher with several shops and the children were encouraged to exploit their talents for art and music.

Lucie Attwell attended a private art school before going on to complete her studies at St Martins School of Art. She married Harold Cecil who worked as an illustrator for publishers Blackie. They had three children, the eldest being Peggy the only girl and possibly the inspiration behind the cute and chubby characters she drew. In 1934 her son Bill died at the age of 20 followed in 1937 by the death of Harold who had struggled manfully as an illustrator despite losing an arm in the Great War.

Amongst Lucie Attwell's prolific output her illustrations for Mother Goose (Raphael Tuck 1910), Alice in Wonderland (Raphael Tuck 1911) and Peter Pan and Wendy (Hodder and Stoughton 1921) shine out.

She died in 1964 but her publishers Dean and Co continued to reprint her work in annuals to 1975, supplemented by illustrations from daughter Peggy.

The annuals were published by SW Partridge until 1932 when Dean took responsibility for further publications. It may be that this is why nobody seems able to trace an annual for 1933 and Partridge and Co had a last bite of the cherry by re-issuing the undated 1932. It would also explain the unusual greeting on the cover of the 1934 published by Dean – Hallo, Here We Are Again. All the children featured on the covers are tots so I have listed just the sex of the child where appropriate.

1922 No 1 Girl on crescent moon	£200
1923 Girl with two puppies	£150
1924 Girl with elf in basket	£150
1925 Girl in tree with puppy	£150
1926 Girl with pup and doll on donkey	£150
1927 Boy and girl astride duck	£150
1928 Child drawn in cart by donkey	£150

1929 Fancy hatted duck in crowd	£150
1930 Policeman halting car/3 bands	£150
1931 Children and pigs in donkey cart	£150
1932 Child playing piano	£150
1933 1932 possibly reissued	
1934 Child greeting reader	£100
1935 Child with umbrella walks pup	£100
1936 Child with bouquet and Boo-Boo	£80
1937 Child walks along with bouquet	£80
1938 Tots look at reader through window	£80
1939 Girl shows off bonneted pup	£80
1940 Children on donkey with pup	£80
1941 Boy gives girl a ride on tricycle	£80
1942 Girls amid flock of birds	£80
1943 Girl carries woolly lamb	£80
1944 Children fish from a boat	£80
1945 Girl peeps into nest	£80
1946 Boy and girl surrounded by pets	£60
1947 Girl waters her garden	£60
1948 Boy and girl greet pets at door	£50
1949 Giraffe in balloon basket	£50
1950 Boy surrounded by flowers	£50
1951 Girls and a boy/snowball/elves	£50
1952 Boy and girl in jampacked boat	£50
1953 Boy/girl holds pixie in left hand at window	£50
1954 Girl and holly, boy and mistletoe	£50
1955 Boy/girl with cat/golly/teddy	£50
1956 Children and toys dance in a ring	£50
1957 Girl with flowers and pixies	£50
1958 Boy cherry picking	£50
1959 Boy/girl carry puppy in basket	£50

The annuals were all dated from 1959 to 1975 when the long run came to an end. You should expect to pay about £40 each for these.

See Joy Book
See Once Upon a Time
See Playbox

Madge Williams

1933 and 1934 (Dean)   £15 each

Magazine for Boys and Girls

1949 – 1956 (Wm Collins)   £5 each

Magic Carpet

1937 and 1938 (Pearson)   £15 each

Magic Fun Book

Both were published by DC Thomson. Magic Fun Book later joined forces with The Beano Book to become Magic-Beano. That was the end of that particular story.

1941 No 1 Koko ice skating	£600
1942 No 2 Koko supporting human pyramid	£600

See Beano

Magic Comic

Publishers DC Thomson had already had remarkable success with The Dandy and The Beano and attempted to follow up with Magic Comic a high quality publication which only ran for 80 issues. There were as you would expect strong contributions from Dudley Watkins (Peter Piper and Gulliver) and Allan Morley (Dolly Dimple). Barry Banger - who later was the star thoroughbred in the Swan publishing stable (see Scramble) – took responsibility for Koko the Pup. Although the comics are scarce I suggest care in investing in them nowadays as prices became inflated in the early 1990's.

No 1 22nd July 1939	£500
Nos 2 – 10	£80 each
Nos 11 – 80	£40 each

Magic Roundabout

An awful lot of people are going to be hunting for these books in a few years' time!

1968 and 1969 (Odhams)	£15 each
1970/80's (Odhams then IPC)	£5 each

Magnet Paper

Just as Gem had provided St Jims as a home for Tom Merry and Co, Magnet introduced us to Greyfriars the setting for the exploits of one Billy Bunter the Owl of the Remove. Frank Richards (Charles Hamilton in real life) wrote copiously for both papers.

The boys' paper ran from 15th February 1908 until it was subsumed into Knock-out comic in 1940. The first issue is worth about £70 today but there is a facsimile so exercise some caution. Other issues to 1940 are worth only £2 to £3 each.

Man from UNCLE

United Network Command for Law Enforcement with Robert Vaughn as Napoleon Solo and David McCallum as Illya Kuryakin.

1966 (Comic Album – World Distributors) Soft covers	£10
1966 - 1969 (World Distributors)	£8 each

Man from UNCLE Adventure Library

14 issues published by World Distributors in 1966	£10 each
1965 – 1969 (Gold Key)	£8 each

Manchester United Football Book

All were published by Stanley Paul.

1967 – 1969	£8 each
1970's	£5 each

Martin's

1935 – 1940 (Lawrence)   £8 each

Marvelman/Young Marvelman

Britain's answer to Superman was created by Mick Anglo - who went on to draw Ace Malloy for Arnold - and later drawn equally superbly by Don Lawrence.

1954 Marvelman standing (Soft covers - Miller)	£45
1954 (Young Marvelman) Hand shake with an alien (Soft covers – Miller)	£30
1955 Marvelman flying (Soft covers – Miller)	£30
1955 (Young Marvelman) Dagger featured with hero (Soft covers – Miller)	£30
1956 – 1960 (Miller)	£15 each
1956 – 1960 (Young Marvelman – Miller)	£15 each
1961 and 1963 (Card covers – Miller)	£12 each
1961 (Young Marvelman Adventures – Miller)	£12
1963 (Marvel Family – Miller)	£15
1963 (Marvelman Jnr – Miller)	£15
1968 (Story Book World Distributors)	£10
1970 – 1971 (World Distributors)	£6 each
1973 – 1974 (IPC)	£5 each
1975 – 1976 (World Distributors)	£5 each
1977 – 1979 (Mighty World of - World Distributors)	£6 each

Marvel Comics – no relation to US company

Publishers L Miller had got themselves into hot water with US National Periodical Publications/DC Comics who were claiming Captain Marvel (1944 - 1954) was a complete rip-off of Superman. Miller avoided a head-on collision by changing their hero's name to Marvelman – sounds worse to me – and that of Captain Marvel Jnr to Young Marvelman but they continued to number the comics from where Captain Marvel had signed off.

Marvelman No 25 (Issue No 1 3rd February 1954)	£20
Young Marvelman No 25 (Issue No 1 3rd February 1954)	£20
Issues 26 – 100 of both titles	£6 each

Issues 101 – 370 of both titles   £3 each

See Captain Marvel

Maverick

All were published by World Distributors.

1961 (Comic Album)   £12
1962 and 1963   £10 each

Merry Moments

1921 – 1926 (Newnes)   £10 each

Mickey Mouse - see Colour Frontispiece

Mickey Mouse is a truly international star. He was of course the creation of Walt Disney who was born in Chicago in 1901.

Two silent films featuring Mickey were created by Disney's small team in 1928 but financial backers considered that there was no room for another animated cartoon with Felix the Cat dominating the market.

Sound was beginning to be introduced into movies in the form of music and a few lines of dialogue. Walt Disney was inspired by the innovations and produced the magical Steamboat Willie which enthralled audiences with its synchronised animation and music.

In 1930 Mickey Mouse began appearing in newspaper strips published by King Features.

British publishers Dean and Sons were quick to realise Mickey's potential and published annuals under licence from 1930. The first three annuals have a coloured frontispiece and three other plates. The others have a coloured frontispiece only. The books had wonderful pictorial spines until they were replaced by cloth in 1944.

1930   £400
1931 – 39   £200 each

1940 and 1941	£150 each
1942	£300
1943	£80
1944 – 1949	£60 each
1950 – 1965	£12 each

Mickey Mouse Weekly

The comics were published by Odhams/Willbank and featured the artwork of Frank Bellamy (Monty Carstairs) and Ron Embleton (Strongbow the Mighty) to name but two.
The word Weekly was dropped from the title from 1942 – 1950.

No 1 8th February 1936	£500
1936 – 1939	£12 each
1940 – 1949	£6 each
1950 – 1957	£3 each

Mighty Comic

| 1954 (Swan) | £6 |

Mrs Hippo's

Amalgamated Press were keen to press home the advantage they had in the comic world via the good offices of Tiger Tim now drawn by Herbert Foxwell. They published a version which they hoped would appeal more to girls. Instead of the Bruin Boys and Tiger Tim they gave us the Hippo Girls and Tiger Tilly.

| 1926 – 1940 (Amalgamated Press) | £15 each |

See Tiger Tim, Playbox, Rainbow, The Bruin Boys

Modern Boy

1931 – 1940 (Boys - Amalgamated Press)	£15 each
1934 – 1936 (Girls - Wm Collins)	£15 each
1940 and 1941 (Book for Boys/Girls - Birn Brothers)	£10 each

Worth a special mention are books written by or having

contributions by WE Johns - better known for his Biggles, Gimlet and Worral stories. These three books were published by Amalgamated Press.

1932 Modern Boys' Book of Aircraft	£40
1936 Modern Boys' Book of Adventure Stories	£40
1939 Modern Boys' Book of Pirates	£120

Modern Boy Comic Paper

All were published by Amalgamated Press

No 1 11th February 1928	£40
Other issues to 1939 (Double price for WE John's Story issues)	£5

Modern Wonder Comic

Flash Gordon first appeared in Modern Wonder No 1 20th May 1939	£20
and in subsequent issues until his "death" in issue No 141	£4 each
All other issues	£3 each

Monster

The Monster Books for Boys/Children/Girls/Tinies were published by Dean from 1930 - 1941, 1943 and 1944 and 1947 -1960

£6 each

Monster Rupert - See Rupert Bear

Mr Pastry's

Mr Pastry was played by Richard Hearne in the 1950's television series.

1958 (A Barker)	£8

See TV Comic

Mrs Hippo

Mrs Hippo's Kindergarten published as a comic strip in the Daily Mirror on 16th April 1904 introduced a new comic culture. This was Tiger Tim's beginning and a great success for publishers Amalgamated Press.

1926 - 1940   £12 each

See Playbox
See Rainbow
See Tiger Tim

Mrs Strang's

Lillian Quiller-Couch was a principal writer and Charles E Brock a main illustrator.

1914 - 1916 (For Children - Frowde/Oxford University Press)	£15 each
1918 - 1926 (For Baby - Hodder and Stoughton/ Oxford University Press)	£15 each
1920 - 1927 (For Girls Humphrey Milford/ Oxford University Press)	£12 each

See Strang's
See Oxford for Girls

Nat Gould

1904 - 1906 (Long)   £10 each

Nelson's

1927 and 1928 (Nelson)   £10 each

Nelson Lee Library

All were published by Amalgamated Press between 1915 and 1933 and are virtually unsaleable today.

No 1 12th June 1915 as a curiosity is worth   £20

All other issues   £2 each

New

They were all published by Amalgamated Press.

1929 – 1931 (Nature Book for Boys and Girls)   £8 each
1932 – 1933 (Zoo Annual for Boys and Girls)   £8 each

Nicholas Thomas

All were published by Sampson Low.

1953 Nicholas and Timothy's Adventure (Strip Book)   £15
1955   £20
1956 (New Big)   £15
1957 (New Big Lucky)   £15

Nister's Holiday

These were all published by Ernest Nister of London but finely printed in Germany. Authors such as E Nesbitt, Constance Lowe and illustrators such as M Rudge, GH Thompson and Dorothy Hardy set extremely high standards.

1888 – 1916 (Nister)   £200 each

Noah's Ark

1934 – 1937 (Amalgamated Press)   £40 each

Noddy Books

Hamsen Van Der Beek was unsurpassed as Noddy illustrator but he was to survive only 4 years after Noddy's beginnings in 1949. These were not annuals but numbered and collectable so they are worth a mention. They were sometimes issued twice yearly by publishers Sampson Low. Prices assume all books have their original dustwrappers. The books were reprinted many times and it is irritating to see books with ISBN numbers - not available until the 1970's – being offered as 1st editions.

No 1 (1949)   £80
Nos 2 – 24 (1950 - 1964)   £50 each

Noddy Strip Books from the 1950's   £25 each

See Enid Blyton

Nursery

1922 – 1932 (The Nursery Book - Nelson)   £45 each

Okay Adventure

1956 – 1959 (TV Boardman) published in dustwrappers £6 each

Once Upon A Time

Flo Lancaster's Great Oojah illustrated by Thomas Maybank features in one of its earliest manifestations. These delightful books also have a series of illustrations by Mabel Lucie Attwell including a full colour plate. Both books were published by E Hulton and Co Ltd of Manchester.

1920 and 1921   £50 each

Oojah

Thomas Maybank's wonderful illustrations of Flo Lancaster's Great Oojah are surely undervalued today. I say buy them when you see them!

1922 (House in title - Daily Sketch London)	£40
1923 – 1926 (Daily Sketch)	£30 each
1927 (Treasure Trunk - Daily Sketch)	£30
1929 – 1931 and 1935 (Uncle Oojah's Big – Allied Newspapers)	£25 each
1933 and 1934 (Uncle Oojah's Big - Daily Sketch and Sunday Graphic)	£25 each
1936 (Allied Newspapers)	£25
1937 – 1942 (Wm Collins)	£20 each
1950 – 1952 (Pitkin)	£10 each

See Joy Book

Oor Wullie

See my remarks about the young genius Dudley D Watkins under The Broons. Oor Wullie first appeared in the Fun Section of the Sunday Post on 8th March 1936 together with Maw and Paw and the bane of Wullie's life PC Murdoch. His pals came along a little later - Fat Bob (1938), Soapy Soutar (1939) and Wee Eck (1945).

All books and comic strips were published by DC Thomson. Anything prior to 1957 is especially difficult to find. The books were encased in thin card wraps and as such were fragile in the extreme. We sold a G/VG copy of the 1943 edition in our May 1999 Auction for £1900 including premium.

1941	£2500
1943	£2000
1949	£800
1953	£350
1955	£350
1957 and 1959	£50
1961, 1963 and 1965	£40 each
1967 and 1969	£25 each
1970's	£8 each
1980's	£4 each

Our Boys/Girls

1930 – 1935 (Boys Tip Top – Renwick)	£10 each
1930 –1941 (Boys/Girls/Kiddies Gift Book – Renwick)	£10 each
1955 (Cowboy – World Distributors)	£10
1955 (Own Schoolgirls – World Distributors)	£5
1956 – 1968 (Own Schoolboys/Schoolgirls – World Distributors)	
Even years	£5 each

Our Darlings

Issues with D Newsome colour plates can make double suggested values.

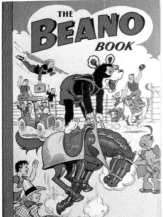

Beano Books left to right

1950 *(top left)*,

1951 *(centre top)* **to**

1959 *(bottom right)*

©DC Thomson and Co. Ltd.

Beano Books left to right
1960 *(top left)* to 1965 *(bottom right)*

©DC Thomson and Co. Ltd.

Dandy Monster Comics left to right
1941 *(top left)* to 1949 *(bottom right)*

Dandy Monster Comics and Books left to right
1950 *(top left)* to 1959 *(bottom right)*

Dandy Books left to right
1960 *(top left)* to 1965 *(bottom right)*

A Collection of British Comics
Left to right
Radio Fun No 1, Film Fun No 1, Lion No 1,
Girl's Crystal, Girl and School Friend
(All © IPC Magazines)
Hotspur Nos 1, 2, and 3
(© DC Thomson and Co. Ltd.)

1882 – 1936 (JF Shaw and Company Ltd London)   £15 each

Our Girls' Best

Published by Epworth Press, dustwrappers by illustrator JP Paterson give the books an added interest for the collector.

1924 – 1926   £10 each

Outer Limits

1967 and 1968 (World Distributors)   £10 each

Outlaws

1962 (Purnell)   £8

Oxford

In 1928 Oxford University Press who had published the Mr and Mrs Strang titles from as early as 1916 published them in their own name Oxford University Press until 1942. The longest survivor was The Oxford Book for Girls.

Also Oxford Book for Scouts 1920 – 1936 and Tiny Folks 1915 – 1937.

Prices are in the £15 - £20 bracket

Partridge's Children's

Publishers SW Partridge and Co were responsible for the early Mabel Lucie Attwell annuals. Louis Wain and George Studdy were drawing for the company's Children's Annual well before 1920.

1909 – 1937 (SW Partridge and Co Victoria)   £30 each

PC 49

PC 49 was drawn by Alan Stranks for Hulton Press's Eagle from 1950 to 1957 but PC Archibald Berkeley-Willoughby had in fact been on the radio since 1947.

1951 – 1953 (PC49, On Duty, On Beat – Juvenile)
  Dustwrappers   £15 each
1954 - 1955 (Cartoon Strip Books Nos 1 and 2
  – Preview)   £12 each
1955 (A Dakers) Dustwrapper   £15

Phantom, The

1965 – 1967 No 1 had card covers (World Distributors)   £6 each

Picture Fun

See Film Fun

Picturegoer

Doubly dated for current and following year, they were all
published by Odhams in dustwrappers.

1950 – 1962   £12 each

Picture Show

These beautiful books were published by Amalgamated Press and
usually included a Who's Who for the year in question. They were
until the advent of the Internet grossly undervalued in the UK but
are selling like hot cakes now with interest from USA.

1927 – 1940   £45 each
1941 - 1950   £15 each
1951 – 1961   £12 each

Pinky and Perky

All were published by Purnell.

1963 – 1969   £8 each
1970's   £4 each

Pip and Squeak

The characters were first introduced to readers of The Daily Mirror on 12th May 1919 through the penmanship of AB Payne who frequently signed his work. Pip the dog, Squeak the female penguin and later Wilfred the rabbit were The Mirror's front line in the circulation wars. Teddy Tail (Daily Mail), Bobby Bear (Daily Herald) and Rupert Bear (Daily Express) all had a serious impact upon the circulations of the newspapers concerned. The Daily Mirror had been the first to produce a comic strip as early as 1904 (See Mrs Hippo). Pip and Squeak Comic Papers ran as a supplement to the newspaper from 1921 to 1925 and today are worth about £4 each.

Artists of considerable quality were recruited by The Daily Mirror, to work on the annuals, AE Bestall and Anne Anderson amongst them. L Church provided excellent cat illustrations from the first issue and Charles Folkard who drew Teddy Tail for the Daily Mail contribute a colour frontispiece in 1924.

The first annual contained a long letter from editor Uncle Dick exhorting children to stick with the book.

1923 – 1940 (Daily Mirror)	£20 each
1954 and 1955 (And Wilfred – Planned Bookselling)	£8 each

Pippin

1968 (TV Publications)	£5
1969 to 1980's (Argus Press)	£3 each

Pippin Comic

No 1 24th September 1966	£10
Other issues to 1975	£2 each

Note that Rupert Bear turned up in Pippin Comic and such issues can fetch £3 - £5 each.

Pixie, Dixie and Mrs Jinks

All were published by World Distributors.

| 1962 | £8 |
| 1973 – 1975 (Hanna-Barbera's) | £6 each |

Playbox

Tiger Tim who had already made his bow at the pen of Julius Stafford Baker in 1904 (Playbox had been given away as a supplement with magazines since the turn of the century. See Mrs Hippo) now had the proper conditions to blossom – his very own colour strip. Baker continued to draw Tim until 1914 when Herbert Foxwell took responsibility for him. Find copies of the 1921 and 1923 annuals for brilliant colour plates by Foxwell depicting Bruin Boys at the Seaside and Bruin Boys' Christmas Morning Concert respectively.

Foxwell's Mrs Bruin, the bespectacled Bear in the mobcap, kept her boys in order only rarely having to brandish a cane.

The very first Playbox Annual had artistic contributions from Louis Wain, Mabel Lucie Attwell and AE Jackson who went on to illustrate a 1913 edition of Alice in Wonderland for Hodder and Stoughton and which now sells for £150.

All were published by Playbox Office at Fleetway House/ Amalgamated Press.

1909 No 1	£60
1910 - 1913	£20 each
1914 – 1930	£20 each
1931 – 1956	£10 each

Playbox Comic

The comic began life as a supplement to Home Chat/World and his Wife/New Children's Encyclopedia.

1898 – 1913 (Issues with Louis Wain illustrations can attract premiums)	£5 each
No 1 (Comic Proper) 14th February 1925	£30
Issues to 1955	£3 each

Took over the original Playhour which ran for only 3 issues as a supplement in 1910 and survived a long time before being subsumed into Jack and Jill in 1955

Playhour

1957 – 1959 (Amalgamated Press)	£5 each
1960 – 1969 (Fleetway)	£5 each
1970/80's	£3 each

Playhour Comic

Having had a short life as a magazine supplement (See Playbox) Playhour rose phoenix-like in 1955 from the Amalgamated Press offices and lived on into the 1990's.

No 1 21st May 1955	£10
All other issues to 1959	£3 each
All other issues	£1 each

Playhour was a voracious guzzler of other titles and variously consumed Chick's Own (1957), Tiny Tots (1959), Harold Hare (1964) and Robin (1969).

Playland

1967 and 1968 (TV Publications)	£5 each
1969 – 1980 when it became part of Pippin	£3 each

Playland Comic

The comic was published by TV Publications.

No 1 13th January 1968	£5
Other issues to 1975	£1 each

Playways

Enid Blyton stories featured in the earlier books.

1954 – 1958 (Little Dot - published by Sunday School Union)	£12 each

1959 - 1966 (Lutterworth)   £5 each

See Enid Blyton and Little Dot

Pleasure Book

1925 (For Boys/Girls - Gordon)   £12 each
1926 - 1929 (Warne's for Boys/Girls –
  Frederick Warne)   £10 each

Pleasure Box

A single issue was published by Robert Hayes Ltd in 1921. The book
published by Geo Goodchild is worth listing for the wonderful
colour plates especially The Hare-Trot frontispiece by Watson
Charlton   £30

Pogles

1967 and 1968 (TV Publications)   £5 each
1969 - 1974 (Argus Press)   £3 each

Pony Club/Magazine

1962 - 1968 (Magazine - Parrish)   £5 each
1967 and 1968 (Club - Parrish)   £5 each
1969 - 1980's (Both publications - Purnell)   £3 each

Pop

All of these little books were published by Kemsley Newspapers -
Daily Sketch and Daily Graphic. Pop was drawn by John Millar Watt.

1925 - 1949   £10 each

Pop Ten (Weekly) Teenbeat

All were published by World Distributors.

1964 - 1971   £4 each

Popeye

EC Segar was the first artist. Bud Sagendorf was the main artist in the 1950's and a daily newspaper comic strip appeared in USA. Popeye, Olive Oyl and Swee'pea were all the rage in the late 1930's and four books appeared in UK published by Birn Bros. I believe all four books were published between 1938 and 1939. I describe the three books published in 1938 and would be glad to learn details of the other one.

1938 Popeye with his eye to a telescope and his foot on a treasure chest	£40
1938 Popeye at ship's wheel with Swee'pea and can of spinach on deck	£40
1938 Popeye and Olive on horseback	£40
1938 or 1939 There was another book published by Birn Bros	£40
1960 (Adprint)	£8
1961 – 1966 (Purnell – artist was George Cattermole)	£8 each
1970/80's (World Distributors/Brown and Watson/Pemberton)	£4 each

Popeye Comics

Dell reprinted Pemberton's USA publications for distribution in the UK.

There were 19 issues between 1951 and 1952	£10 each
World Distributors published 7 issues in 1957	£8 each
Miller published 30 issues between 1959 and 1963	£6 each

See Jolly, Film Fun and TV Comics

Popular Book of Stories

All were published by Amalgamated Press.

1930 – 1940 (Boys/Girls)	£8 each

Pow!

1968 – 1971 (Odhams)	£5 each
1971 – 1972 (IPC)	£5 each

Pow! Comic

Ken Reid's Dare-a Day Davy held the back page from the first issue. Mike Higgs drew The Cloak which later turned up in Smash. The comics were published by Odhams and then by Fleetway.

No 1 21st January 1967	£10
Other issues to 1968	£2 each

Became part of Wham

Preview

1946 – 1953 (World Film) Dustwrappers	£5 each
1954 – 1962 (Adprint)	£5 each
1963 (Golden Pleasure)	£5

Princess (Tina) Ballet

1962 – 1968 (Fleetway)	£4 each
1969 (Tina introduced to title – Fleetway)	£4
1970's (IPC)	£3 each

Princess Gift Book for Girls

1961 – 1969 (Fleetway)	£4 each
1970's (IPC)	£3 each

Princess (Tina) Pony Book

1963 – 1965 (Fleetway)	£4 each
1969 (Tina added to title – Fleetway)	£4
1970/80's (IPC)	£3 each

Princess Tina

1969 (Fleetway)	£4

1970/80's (IPC)   £3 each

Princess (Tina) Comics

All came from Amalgamated Press/Fleetway/IPC.

No 1 (Princess) 30th January 1960   £10
All other issues to 1967   £2 each

Took over Girl in 1964

No 1 (Princess Tina) 23rd September 1967   £10
All other issues to 1969   £2 each

Prize Budget for Girls/Boys

All were published by Blackie.

1934 – 1943   £10 each

Puck

1921 and 1923 –1925 (Puck Office/Fleetway House)   £20 each
1922 and 1926 – 1941 (Amalgamated Press)   £20 each

Puck Comic

SJ Cash's Fairy Farm appeared to have a lot in common with Mrs
Bruin and her boys. Why change a winning formula? All were
published by Amalgamated Press for whom SJ Cash had worked on
Playbox.

No 1 30th July 1904   £40
Other issues to May 1940   £5 each

Subsumed into Sunbeam

Punch and Judy

1932 –1935 (Children's – Newnes)   £25 each
1955 (Juvenile)   £8

Radio Fun

Big Hearted Arthur Askey was drawn by Reg Parlett from 1938. All were published by Amalgamated Press until 1960 (Fleetway).

1940	£100
1941 - 1945	£45 each
1946 -1949	£20 each
1950 - 1959	£10 each
1960	£12

Radio Fun Comic

George the Jolly Gee Gee was the work of genius Roy Wilson but was not a radio character at all. He started on the front page of the very first issue and continued until replaced by Arthur Askey. In a wonderful piece of symmetrical thinking publishers Amalgamated Press let George have the cover to himself in the final issue in 1961. See Colour Plates

No 1 15th October 1938	£250
Nos 2 - 10	£40 each
Nos 11 - 100	£10 each
Other issues to 1961	£5 each

Took over Wonder in 1953 before itself being subsumed into Buster

Railway

All were published by Wm Collins.

1929 - 1932	£12 each

Rainbow

Rainbow was another vehicle for Amalgamated Press's popular Tiger Tim who featured in the pages of the comic from 1914 to 1956 and in the annual from 1924 to 1957. A nice touch was that Rainbow was edited by Mrs Bruin who had boarded the animals – known as the Bruin Boys - once they left Mrs Hippo's Kindergarten.

1924 No 1   £45
Other annuals to 1940   £15 each
Other annuals to 1957   £10 each

See Playbox and Mrs Hippo

Rainbow Comic

Tiger Tim and the Bruin Boys drawn most notably by Herbert
Foxwell appeared in the comic throughout this Amalgamated Press
publication's run.

No 1 14th February 1914   £30
Other issues to 1956   £5 each

Took over Tiger Tim's Weekly in 1940 and was eventually subsumed
into Tiny Tots

Raymond Glendenning's Book of Sport for Boys

1950 – 1953 (Sportsguide)   £5 each
1954 and 1955 (Planned Bookselling)   £5 each
1956 – 1961 (A Dakers)   £5 each

Riders of the Range

1952 - 1956 (Juvenile)   £15
1957 – 1960 (Eagle added to title – E Hulton)
   Dustwrappers   £15 each
1961 and 1962 (Longacre)   £15 each

Robin

Eagle's younger brother was aimed at very young children. The first
annual contained Happy New Pictures, Stories, Poems and Puzzles.

1954 – 1960 (E Hulton and Co Ltd) dustwrappers   £8 each
1961 – 1964 (Longacre)   £6 each
1965 – 1970 (Odhams)   £4 each
1970's (IPC)   £3 each

Robin Comic

Mary Adams' Andy Pandy was the front page star of Robin Comic from 1953 to 1969 having made his debut on BBC's Watch with Mother in 1950.

No 1 28th March 1953   (E Hulton and Co Ltd)   £40
Other issues to 1969 (Added Story Time 1967
    – Hulton/Longacre/IPC)   £3 each

Subsequently taken over by Playhour

Robin Hood

1957 – 1959 (Amalgamated Press)   £10 each
1960 (Fleetway)   £10

See Adventures of Robin Hood

Robin Hood Comics and Papers

1901 – 1906 There were 88 issues published by Aldine about A5 size.
No 1 is worth £10 confirmed by our May 1999 auction but there is
    little interest in the rest   £2 each
Robin Hood also appeared in over 50 Thriller
    Library Comics   £10 each
1957 – 1958 (Robin Hood/Robin Hood Tales
    - Miller) 34 issues   £6 each

See Thriller Picture Library

Rosebud

All were published by Clarke.

1881 – 1924   £15 each

Rover

All were published by DC Thomson.

1926 Boys on cross country run   1927 Rodeo Cowboy and horse
1928 Boys in car reg OK 1234   1929 Two boys on camels
1930 Lad pulling boys in rickshaw   1931 Two boys in speedboat and two water planing
1932 Two boys and dog hitchhiking   1933 Man on motorbike chasing zebra
1934 Two naval officers and rabbit   1935 Two naval officers mock Chinese barber
1936 Two boys by tropical pool   1937 Cowboys playing football
1938 Cowboy suffers rope dentistry   1939 Two lumberjacks on log
1940 Mountie on moose avoids wolves 1941 Lumberjacks race on log and skis
1942 Two men play tropical darts   1950 Blacksmith works on robot
1956 Globe surrounded by stars   1957 Title in horizontal stripes – aeroplane picture
1958 As 1957 but American Indian   1959 Crashed aeroplane in the mountains

Rover Comic Paper

Rover was one of the Big Five titles published by DC Thomson. Although it was clearly a paper to begin with it shifted its ground over the years realising the demand amongst the readership for comic strips. Allan Morley's Nosey Parker who made his bow in 1925 and achieved front page status by 1942 was a case in point.

I Flew with Braddock by George Bourne and Peter Sutherland's Alf Tupper - The Tough of the Track – are stories most fondly remembered.

The comic appeared fortnightly between 1941 and 1949.

No 1 4th March 1922	£150
Issues 1922 – 1939	£8 each
Issues 1940 – 1949	£5 each
Issues 1950 – 1959	£4 each
Issues 1960 – 1969	£2 each
Issues 1970 – 1973	£1 each

Took over Adventure (1961) and Wizard (1963) but Wizard fought back and subsumed Rover in 1973

Roy of the Rovers

A publication out of the Tiger stable, Roy was written by Stewart Colwyn (Frank Pepper) and illustrated by Joe Colquhoun.

| 1958 and 1959 (Amalgamated Press) | £18 each |
| 1960 – 1969 (Fleetway) | £10 each |

1970/80's (IPC)   £4 each

Roy of the Rovers Comic

Roy just had to go on and when he could no longer play he became
Melchester's manager. All were published by Fleetway/IPC.

No 1 25th September 1976   £10
Other issues to 1990's   £1 each

Roy Rogers

All were published by World Distributors. The King of the Cowboys
also appeared continuously from 1944 to 1957 in Wonder, TV Comic
and Sun respectively.

1952 – 1958 (Cowboy)	£12 each
1954 (Stories - Adprint)	£8
1955 – 1962 Numbered 1 – 8	£12 each
1960, 1962, 1964 and 1966 (Cowboy)	£10 each

Roy Rogers (and Trigger)

Dell reprinted 100 Pemberton/World Distributors titles between
1951 and 1959 for distribution in the UK   £8 each

Rupert Bear

Rupert Bear was The Daily Express's response to the highly
successful children's strips in other newspapers. Teddy Tail, Bobby
Bear and Tiger Tim had boosted the circulations of their
respective organs and now it was Rupert's turn.

Herbert Tourtel born in 1874 had poetic aspirations and had risen
to senior executive at The Daily Express. His wife Mary born in the
same year was already an established book illustrator. Her first
book, A Horse Book in the Dumpy Books for Children Series
published by Grant Richards in 1901, is worth about £150. Her book
Three Little Foxes published in 1903 in the same Series sold in our
October 1999 Auction for £150.

Mary Tourtel was the obvious choice to illustrate the new strip whilst Herbert wrote the stories in simple verse bordering on doggerel.

Little Lost Bear ran for 36 days in The Daily Express starting on 8th November 1920. The stories appeared in book form published by Thos Nelson the following year. This notion of publishing newspaper strips in book form was to become from 1936 the way in which Daily Express Rupert Annuals were created. Sometimes Rupert was replaced by stories about Margot also by Tourtel but Rupert was the favoured character amongst the readership.

Mary and Herbert travelled widely together and it was in Germany in 1931 that Herbert Tourtel died from a heart condition. Mary as one would expect was deeply affected. They had been devoted to each other and had no children.

She continued to write and illustrate the stories herself until failing eyesight forced her to retire in 1935. The last story she wrote for the newspaper was Rupert and Bill's Seaside Holiday. She died in 1948.

Alfred Edmeades Bestall MBE born in 1892 was a natural successor. He had already published cartoons in such prestigious magazines as Punch and The Tatler as well as drawing the covers for Schoolgirl's Own Annuals. In 1927 he had illustrated The Play's the Thing for Enid Blyton – a book worth about £100 today in its original dustwrapper.

Bestall both drew the Rupert panels and wrote the stories himself until 1965. His first newspaper story Rupert Algy and the Smugglers appeared on 28th June 1935 and was reprinted in the second Rupert Annual in 1937.

At the beginning Alfred Bestall felt that he was cramping his natural style in trying to make a smooth transition from Mary Tourtel's work and admitted that inconsistencies did creep into the plots. In fact he was always ready to criticise his own work. He thought that the 1942 Annual cover as well as being poorly printed was badly composed and was aware that Rupert and Dinkie (1955) had a plot which relied too much on the conjuror and too little on Rupert. He also admitted to having "created" inadvertently a character that already existed in another paper – Willie Whiskers who appeared in the 1945 Annual. Once he realised the error he discarded the Whiskers and gradually eliminated the character altogether in favour of his country mouse cousin Rastus who appeared in the 1946 Annual. Willie did return however in later years without his surname.

The first three annuals were printed in black and according to Alfred a rather smudgy red and for the 1953 Annual the editorial team of which he was a part decided to reproduce a couple of these stories – The Cannibals (1936) and Mysteryland (1938) – in full colour. Such was the outcry from parents who had passed annuals on to their children that the experiment was not repeated until the special anniversary issue in 1985.

Choosing stories for the annuals has always been a difficult process. There was to be no overlapping of plots, scenes or characters and the stories should be set in a different season of the year. The same principles apply today and Ian Robinson, Rupert Editor and story writer since 1989, tries to run the stories through from Spring to Christmas.

Bestall was said to have continued the sound principles on which Mary Tourtel had based her charming character very much aware of his responsibility to his young readers. He may even have taken things further than necessary. When asked about Rupert and the Stolen Apples he quickly said it was not a title of his because he would avoid any suggestion in his stories that stealing even existed. But did Tourtel in her Rupert stories create a world which was so ideal after all? I suggest a look at the covers would be enough to persuade you otherwise – the wolf in the bed, ogres, escaping capture, hiding in the copper.

One of John Harrold's favourite frames is from Rupert in Dreamland when Rupert's ostrich steed nonchalantly disposes of the irritating, talking teapot with a healthy kick.

Children would often write to Bestall and one boy submitted a picture of The Little Plane to which the artist added a driving handle but otherwise used without alteration in the 1941 newspaper story. It reappeared in the Annuals for 1942, 1943, 1949 and 1967.

Another frequent request was for the artist to draw a comprehensive map of Nutwood but Alfred Bestall resisted saying he hadn't the pluck to annoy his geologist friends. The endpaper for the 1967 Annual was as far as he was prepared to go.

He did not write many sequels but Rupert and Mr Punch (1948 Newspaper/1951 Annual) followed on from Rupert and Dog Toby (1936/1937) and the more humorous Rupert and the Early Bird (1958/1971) was a sequel to Rupert and the Jackdaw (1958/1967). Following Bestall's retirement from newspaper work in 1965 children's editor Frederick Chaplain wrote the stories and Alex Cubie illustrated them and they did create sequels in the interests of continuity.

Controversy arrived in 1973 in the shape of the annual for that year. Several children had enquired as to why Rupert always had a brown face on the annual cover but a white face inside the book. The Chairman at The Daily Express decided to try the other effect. This was done without Bestall's consent. Putting Rupert's face against a nearly white sky made a weak composition that he did not like. He ordered the printers to remove his signature as far as possible. It can however still be seen as a pink blur to the rear cover just above Housemouse's foot. Bestall reflected ironically that sales were unaffected by the dispute but vowed to do no more colour work.

Rupert was clearly a tremendous success for the newspaper. The Rupert League created in 1932 was a club which issued a metal badge and a membership card upon which children could collect merit tokens. Members received a birthday card each year. There was also a Scottish version of the club. Membership of the League rose to one million in three years and the idea was eventually dropped because of the high administration costs.

Various printers were employed to print the annuals and some collectors try to acquire each printing of a particular book. We have sold a few proof copies from the printers LTA Robinson which had card covers with penned instructions. The 1951 Annual requested 1,000,000 copies and that was from just one printing house.

Alex Cubie had already been working on the Adventure Series and on Bestall's retirement from story work he assumed the responsibility for illustrating the newspaper strips. The stories were now written by Freddie Chaplain until illness forced him to retire and he was succeeded by James Henderson as Rupert Editor.

Alex was born in 1911 and in the 1930's had worked as a cartoonist for The Daily Sketch. He worked as an artist at The Daily Express from 1951. He died in 1995.

Cubie provided the Rupert annual covers and endpapers from 1974 to 1977.

John Harrold who was born in 1947 first drew Rupert in 1973 for Fun To Cook With Rupert published by Collins in 1974. His first annual work was in 1976 when he contributed the unsigned Rupert's School-Time Game and Rupert's Kite Puzzle.

John Harrold never worked with Alfred Bestall or Alex Cubie although his first story Rupert and the Worried Elves appeared in the newspaper as early as 14th October 1976. His first editor Frederick Chaplain was keen for John Harrold to work in the style appropriate to Alex Cubie. He wanted a broken, thicker line which left out fine detail. John felt frustrated by the conflicting advice from Chaplain who sent him copious contradictory cuttings of the same characters.

James Henderson who had worked for The Express since 1952 took over responsibility for Rupert from an ailing Freddie Chaplain. Henderson was happy to see Harrold impose his own style on the stories which he most readily and successfully did. Jim Henderson claimed the 1985 Annual covers to be a complete masterpiece uniting 65 years of Rupert history.

John Harrold has the same requests to draw a map of Nutwood – more from adults these days than children - that so plagued

Bestall. His response is not dissimilar. He points out that the interior, the location and even the windows of Rupert's house change periodically so what about the whole panorama which runs from the wood to the seaside and to the exotic East? He was once invited by the Express to produce a map of Nutwood which he began to see as a semi-aerial view with all four seasonal elements displayed but the project was never developed.

Characters have changed over the years and indeed within the years. Rupert's mother and father grew older and younger under Bestall's penmanship – at times they looked positively geriatric compared to their young son. They are now of a decidedly believable generation.

So how old is Rupert? John says he is about 7 because his young readership – excluding adult collectors of course - like to look up to heroes and heroines who are a bit older than themselves. He believes Rupert to be a character upon whom the reader can impose their own ideology and that to define him too specifically would prevent people of both sexes and all ages from seeing the world through his eyes.

John Harrold and Rupert Editor Ian Robinson maintain the same high standards as their predecessors with regard to the expectations of children. They are most concerned with a story which has narrative and illustrative continuity. Long may they both continue.

The Annuals

Rupert Bear Annuals were published by The Daily Express from 1936 and were not dated until 1958. See Colour Plates

1936 with dustwrapper	£2000	1936 without d/w	£350
1937	£300	1938	£300
1939	£350	1940	£350
1941	£450	1942	£500
1943	£350	1944	£300
1945	£250	1946	£200
1947	£200	1948	£80
1949	£80	1950	£120
1951 – 1955	£80	1956	£120
1957	£70	1958 and 1959 (Dated)	£70 each

Annuals from 1960 – 1968 had Magic Painting (MP) pages. If these are completed or even partially done it has a serious impact on the value of the book. Prices are quoted for books with MP done and MP undone in VG condition. If a book is in less than VG condition then it's really of no significance whether the MP's are done or not. Remember that Fine or Mint examples of these books with MP's untouched are greatly sought after.

1960	MP done	£40	MP untouched	£100
1961	MP done	£40	MP untouched	£100
1962	MP done	£40	MP untouched	£100
1963	MP done	£40	MP untouched	£100
1964	MP done	£40	MP untouched	£100
1965	MP done	£40	MP untouched	£100
1966	MP done	£40	MP untouched	£100
1967	MP done	£30	MP untouched	£80
1968	MP done	£20	MP untouched	£60
1969		£20		

Annuals from the 1970's are pretty common in Very Good condition and are only worth £4 - £5 each. However Very Fine or Mint editions are becoming more difficult to find and may be worth as much as £30 each. All these annuals are dated to the title page. The books for 1970 and 1971 are more difficult to find than the others. Virtually impossible to find is the brown faced 1973 Annual. There are supposed to be only a handful in existence. The likely market price would be £5000 plus.

Books from the 1980's are much scarcer than the 70's in Fine condition or better and can be seen at £20 each. These books are either dated or numbered. When you know that 1985 was No. 50 you can work out the others. 1988 is dated to the rear endpaper.

1990's annuals in Mint condition could prove a good investment at around £10 each.

Annuals from 1978 to the present day signed by John Harrold attract premium prices.

Early Collectable Rupert Books

Listed below you will find reference to all the really collectable Rupert titles to 1974. The Rupert Chronology which appears at the end of the Rupert section attempts to simplify matters for the collector.

The following four little books were reprinted from stories in The Daily Express and were published by Thomas Nelson of London, Edinburgh and New York. See Colour Plates for two of them

The Adventures of Rupert Little Lost Bear 1921	£850
Little Bear and the Fairy Child 1922	£950
Little Bear and the Ogres 1922	£950
Margot the Midget 1922	£850

The following three books, published by Sampson and Lowe have pictorial spines and front cover plates applied to matt boards. You could be forgiven for thinking they had been rebound. Prices quoted apply to any edition even though the books were reprinted later in the 1920's.

Rupert Little Bears Adventures No 1 1924	
(See Colour Plates)	£850
Rupert Little Bears Adventures No 2 1924	£800
Rupert Little Bears Adventures No 3 1925	£800

A Monster Problem

There is a great deal of confusion about Monster Ruperts. We get phone calls almost daily from people who think they have unearthed a treasure. Let's sort it out once and for all.

The genuinely collectable Monsters were published by Sampson Low in the 1930's. As you can see from the colour plates at the centre of this guide, they had thick pictorial spines. Each has a coloured frontispiece identical to the picture on the front cover.

In the late 1940's and early 50's four other Monsters appeared also published by Sampson Low. Three of the books were green and one was yellow. They all had cloth spines. The yellow book shows Rupert confronting a wolf, Red Riding Hood style. One green one has Rupert consulting a lizard with a bicycle. The other two pale green books both feature Rupert, Edward and Bill on the cover assisting a boy from a hole. These two books had cut outs – 200 and 120 respectively although if you count them you will get a surprise.

All four of these books are worth £30 - £40 each in VG but you often see them priced much higher by confused vendors. They are reasonably hard to find in their original dust wrappers and the price could be double.

Monster Ruperts – the original series

Monster Rupert 1931 Black Cover (See Colour Plates)	£900
Monster Rupert 1932 Red cover	£800
Monster Rupert 1933 Green Cover	£800
Monster Rupert 1934 Orange Cover (See Colour Plates)	£800

Rupert Little Bear Series

Published by Sampson Low in 1925 these little books again have a colour plate applied to the front board. The spines are cloth and bear the title. The books were reprinted and these have the series titles to rear boards. There is no difference in the value of the first editions and the reprints.

Rupert and the Magic Toy Man	£600
Rupert and the Old Miser	£600
Rupert and the Princess	£600
Rupert and the Magic Key/Brigands	£600
Rupert in Dreamland	£600

Three Scarce Rupert Titles

Each one has a pictorial spine. The first two titles were reprinted around 1941 with cloth spines which were only about an inch thick. Such reprints sell for about £40 each.

Rupert Story Book 1938	£450
Rupert Little Bear More Stories 1939	£450
Rupert Again 1940 (See Colour Plates)	£450

Pop-Ups

The Daily Express between 1931 and 1935 published six Children's Annuals with pop-ups. Rupert popped up in three of them.

1930 No 1 with Castle to cover	£100
1931 No 2 with Rodeo character to cover	£100
1935 Living Models with Duck to cover	£100

Rupert also featured in the other three.

1932 No 3 with Elephant's head to cover	£90
1933 No 4 with Pelican to cover	£90
1934 No 5 with Golly to cover	£90

Rupert Little Bear Library

There were 46 titles printed and reprinted in the late 20's to mid 30's. The titles available are listed inside the front cover. When the last title listed coincides with the number of the book you are holding, congratulations you have got the first edition. These flimsy yellow books usually turn up minus their spines and in that condition are worth around £10. A VG example of any of the 46 is now £50 - £60. If you are lucky enough to find one in a dustwrapper expect to pay £130 - £150. Reprints are worth £30 each.

Another source of confusion

A series of 18 yellow Little Bear Libraries were issued through Woolworths in the 1970's. These books were published in two series with both hard and soft laminated covers. They are much smaller than the original series and have a coloured Rupert to the spine. The complete set of 18 should be available for about £40

Rupert Adventure Series - described by A E Bestall as The Quarterlies

Although AE Bestall wrote a few stories for the Adventure Series and was responsible for the early covers, the idea had been for him to take the project on single-handed. In the event he saw the task as too onerous and refused so the early numbers were nearly all reprinted from annuals. As the annual stories became too long for the Adventure Series, Frederick Chaplain, children's editor at the time, found himself under increasing pressure to create stories especially for them. Young Enid Ash was brought in to assist Alex Cubie with the artwork and drew some of the front and back covers although Bestall is reputed to have drawn several of the character heads for her.

Bestall could never arouse much enthusiasm for the project. He considered the later covers to be too similar and the printing quality to be poor. WH Smith was losing interest so the Series ended.

There are 50 titles to collect and each book is clearly numbered. They were originally priced at 1/- to the front cover although we have unearthed a few copies from New Zealand which bear 1/3d. The series ran from 1948 to 1963 before running out of steam. Oddly therefore it is the later titles which are hardest to find as the print runs were presumably much smaller.

Rupert Adventure Series No 1 (Rupert and Snuffy)	£40
Rupert Adventure Series Nos 2 – 9	£15
Rupert Adventure Series No 10 (Stray Puppy)	£25
Rupert Adventure Series Nos 11 –29	£20
Rupert Adventure Series Nos 30 – 39	£25
Rupert Adventure Series Nos 40 – 48	£50
Rupert Adventure Series No 49	£100
Rupert Adventure Series No 50	£120

None of the above should be confused with 1975 bluey/grey publications Adventure Books Nos 1 and 2. They cost 15p each originally and are worth about £5 each today.

Similar Publications

There are a few publications in the same format as the Adventure Series. Most commonly there is Rupert Activity Book No 2 – nobody knows what happened to No 1. The puzzles are usually done but if you can find a clean one it's worth £45.

Then there's the rare Music Book No 2 (See Colour Plates) also published by Oldbourne and in that same year 1959. It has the Adventure Series No 39 picture to the cover but cost 2/6. We have seen a teacher's edition of this book so it was obviously produced for schools and presumably was discarded when tatty. We know of only two copies extant. The chances of finding one are slim but if you do it'll be £700 or more.

Incidentally in 1960 Oldbourne published a couple of large format, paper cover titles
Rupert and the Pink Kitten
Rupert and Dickory Dock
which are worth £35 each in Fine condition. A large number appeared in unissued condition from an Essex shop clearance in the late 1980's or they'd be worth a lot more.

In 1949 Sampson Low published two Famous Yellow Library titles in Adventure Series format with yellow covers and black and white contents

Rupert and his Friend Margot   £40
Rupert, the Knight and the Lady   £40

1946 saw the publication of Rupert and the Wonderful Boots also by Sampson Low. Large format with card covers   £45

Sampson Low also published Rupert Stories the cover of which shows Rupert buying cakes in a shop. They're worth about £20 – the books not the cakes. As this book was published in 1947 it is possible to show that Purnell were not the only ones to be shadowing the Express Annuals from the late 1940's to the early 1950's. Just look at the Rupert Chronology section below.

Cut-Outs

These two titles appeared in soft covers and greatly different formats. See Colour Plates

Rupert and the Snow Man 1950 with all cut-outs intact   £500
Rupert and Edward and the Circus 1949 with all cut-outs intact £200

The Purnell "Annuals"

Publishers Purnell and Sons held the rights to some Mary Tourtel stories and were not slow to appreciate Rupert's enormous popularity and saleability. They printed several "Annuals" of their own but were not allowed to name them as such. Alfred Bestall saw these books as rival publications but they have never really caught the collector's imagination and are available at £15 - £20 each.

I have used a certain amount of creative guesswork based on previous owners' inscriptions in compiling the list but this would appear to have been the chronology. The first three titles were issued through Marks and Spencer.

1947 Rupert Cover shows Rupert being hidden in a boiler by maid goose

1948 Rupert Cover shows fox talking to Rupert and Bill from a tree

1949 Rupert Cover shows Rupert astride white stallion. Contained cut-outs

1950 Rupert Story Book Covers were glazed green with Rupert dashing towards his mother with Bill and Edward in plane. The first edition had 4 colour plates to centre of the book.

1951 The Big Rupert Story Book Covers show Rupert and a witch in a flying basket

1952 Rupert Little Bear Scary man chases Rupert, Margot and the Gnome

1953 The New Rupert Colour Story Book Covers show Mother and Rupert shopping for treats

Purnell continued to publish Rupert and maintained their association with Marks and Spencer with The St Michael Book of Rupert Favourites which had five versions from 1977 – 1981. By now the Tourtel stories had been reprinted so many times that they were redrawn and coloured by office artists. The first four were numbered as First, Second etc. They are worth about £6 each.

LTA Robinson Publications

LTA Robinson printed a number of Rupert Annuals but were also responsible for a number of books containing Mary Tourtel reprints. It seems to me they were on the Annual bandwagon too - quite within their rights of course. They are available at around £20 each.

1953 Rupert Picture Story Book Covers show Rupert hiking to Joy Valley accompanied by gnome on hare's back

1954 The New Rupert Colour Adventure Book Cover shows Rupert aboard Dapple with the Prince

1955 Rupert Adventure Book Cover shows Rupert abseiling castle with guards in background

1956 Rupert Colour Adventure Book Cover shows turbaned gent with Rupert and Bill

Worth a serious mention

Fine copies of the following 1950's titles could be £80 - £100 each

Rupert Gets Captured
Rupert at the Seaside (See Colour Plates)
Rupert Tracing and Painting Book
Rupert Painting Book made and printed by LTA Robinson
Rupert and the Enchanted Princess

Facsimile Rupert Annuals

First published by The Daily Express in 1985 the Rupert Facsimiles have gone from strength to strength. The dustwrappered facsimile for 1936 originally cost £4.95 and now sells for £100. Only 15000 numbered editions were printed of the first three books. The issues for 1939 - 1941 were published by Annual Concepts Ltd and were not numbered. We believe that only 7000 were produced for each of 1942 - 1945 and 1948/1949. Many collectors have opted for facsimiles for the early years but were disappointed to learn that facsimiles for 1946 and 1947 were not to be published because of sensitive socio-political content. Pedigree had already made changes to the 1942 facsimile to make it more politically acceptable.

1936 Mint in dustwrapper	£100
1937 Mint	£80
1938 Mint	£100
1939 Mint	£30
1940 Mint	£20
1941 Mint in slipcase	£20
1942 Mint in slipcase	£50
1943 Mint in slipcase	£20
1944 Mint in slipcase	£20
1945 Mint in slipcase	£20
1948 Mint in slipcase	£20
1949 Mint in slipcase	£20

Rupert Ephemera

At our Auctions over the past few years we have been struck by the enthusiasm of Rupert collectors for certain items of ephemera relating to the little bear. Here is a brief guide to prices realised for some of them

Rupert Wedgwood 1988 Tankard	£170
Rupert League Metal Badge 1932	£40
Rupert League Membership Card 1932	£140
Rupert League Member's Birthday Card	£65
Rupert Scottish League Membership Card	£160
A E Bestall original letter	£380
Rupert Cutlery Set 1972 boxed	£160
Rupert Bear Box of Tissues 1970's	£75

Rupert Bear Book Chronology to 1974

1921	Adventures of Rupert The Little Lost Bear (Nelson)
1922	Little Bear and the Fairy Child (Nelson)
	Little Bear and the Ogres (Nelson)
	Margot the Midget (Nelson)
1924	Little Bear's Adventures No 1 (Sampon Low, Marston)
	Little Bear's Adventures No 2 (Sampson Low, Marston)

1925	Rupert and the Magic Toy Man (Sampson Low, Marston)
	Rupert and the Old Miser (Sampson Low, Marston)
	Rupert and The Princess (Sampson Low, Marston)
	Rupert and The Magic Key (Sampson Low, Marston)
	Rupert in Dreamland (Sampson Low, Marston)
	Little Bear's Adventures No 3 (Sampson Low, Marston)
1928 – 1936	Rupert Little Bear Library Nos 1 – 46 (Sampson Low, Marston)
1930	Daily Express Children's Annual
1931	Daily Express Children's Annual
	Monster Rupert (Sampson Low, Marston)
1932	Daily Express Children's Annual
	Monster Rupert (Sampson Low, Marston)
1933	Monster Rupert (Sampson Low, Marston)
	Daily Express Children's Annual
1934	Daily Express Children's Annual
	Monster Rupert (Sampson Low, Marston)
1935	Daily Express Children's Annual
1936 – 1939	Daily Express Boys and Girls' Books x 4 large format
	£30 each (£50 in d/ws)
1936	Rupert Annuals (Daily Express)
1938	Rupert Story Book (Sampson Low, Marston)
1939	Rupert Little Bear More Stories (Sampson Low, Marston)
1940	Rupert Again (Sampson Low, Marston)
1941	Rupert Story Book and Rupert Little Bear More Stories
	Reprints (Sampson Low, Marston)
1946	Rupert and the Wonderful Boots (Sampson Low)
1947	Rupert Stories (Sampson Low)
	Rupert (Purnell)
1948	Rupert (Purnell)
1949	Rupert (Purnell)
1948 – 1950	Monster Ruperts x 4 (Sampson Low)
1948 – 1963	Rupert Adventure Series (Daily Express/Odhams/Purnell)
1949	Rupert Tracing and Painting Book (Sampson Low)
	Rupert Painting Book (Robinson)
	Rupert Famous Yellow Library x 2 (Sampson Low)
	Rupert Edward and the Circus (Sampson Low)
1950	Rupert and the Snowman (Sampson Low)
	Rupert Story Book (Purnell)
1951	Rupert Gets Captured (Sampson Low)
	The Big Rupert Story Book Published (Purnell)

1952	Rupert at the Seaside (Sampson Low)
	Rupert and the Enchanted Princess (Sampson Low)
	Rupert Little Bear (Purnell)
1953	The Rupert Picture Story Book (Robinson)
	The New Rupert Colour Story Book (Purnell)
1954	The New Rupert Colour Adventure Book (Robinson)
1955	Rupert Adventure Book (Robinson)
1956	Rupert Colour Adventure Book (Robinson)
1959	Rupert Activity Book No 2 (Daily Express/Oldbourne)
	Rupert Music Book No 2 (Daily Express/Oldbourne)
1960	Rupert and the Pink Kitten (Odhams)
	Rupert and Dickory Dock (Odhams)
1974	Lots of Fun to Cook with Rupert (Collins)

Saint, The

Simon Templar made his first appearance in Leslie Charteris' Meet The Tiger in 1928. If asked to put a face to the character these days the image of the debonair Roger Moore would come to most people's minds after his dashing 1960's TV portrayal. In 1966 Panther published the Roger Moore Adventure Book which sells today at £10.

1967 – 1969 (World Distributors)	£15 each
1979 and 1980 (Pemberton)	£4 each

See Super Detective Library

School and Adventure for Boys/Girls

All were published by Epworth Press.

1929 – 1937	£8 each

Schoolboys

1923 (United Society Christian Literature)	£10
1924 – 1936 (Wm Collins)	£10 each
1925 – 1940 (Religious Tract Society/Boys Own Paper)	£8 each
1941 (Lutterworth)	£8
1926 (Adventure Book – Aldine)	£10

1945 (Adventures – Swan)	£8
1946 – 1958 (Album – Swan)	£8 each
1968 (World Distributors)	£5
1970/80's (World Distributors)	£3 each

School Friend

All were published by Amalgamated Press/Fleetway/IPC. See Colour Plates

1927 – 1949	£15 each
1950 – 1959	£10 each
1960 – 1969	£5 each
1970/80's	£4 each

School Friend Comic

Evelyn Flinders' The Silent Three appeared for 13 years from the first issue. All were published by Amalgamated Press/Fleetway.

| No 1 20th May 1950 | £50 |
| Other issues to 1965 | £2 each |

Took over Girls' Crystal in 1963 before being subsumed into June in 1965

Schoolgirls

1923 (United Society Christian Literature)	£10
1924 – 1936 (Wm Collins)	£10 each
1925 – 1940 (Religious Tract Society)	£8 each
1941 (Lutterworth)	£8
1945 – 1957 (Album – Swan) See Schoolboys – Girls didn't have adventures!	£8 each
1968 (World Distributors)	£5
1970/80's (World Distributors)	£3 each

Schoolgirl Comic

This title had a short run for publishers Shurey but was revived by Amalgamated Press some six years later.

No 1 21st February 1922   £15
Other Charles Shurey issues to 1923   £5 each
No 1 3rd August 1929   £20
Other Amalgamated Press issues to 1940   £5 each

Took over Schoolgirls Own in 1936 and was eventually subsumed into Girls' Crystal in 1940

Schoolgirls Own

The 1928 Annual includes Who's Who at Morcove School. It runs from Miss Alice Edith Somerfield, M.A., F.R.G.S. Headmistress to Dame Steggles who keeps the tuck shop just by the school gates and to Ursula Wade a spiteful sneak for whom nobody cares.

Several early covers were illustrated by AE Bestall more famous for Rupert Bear. The 1926 edition has a story attributed to Hilda Richards who wrote Bessie Bunter of Cliff House School under the same name. Hilda was of course Charles Hamilton. The argument rages as to whether Hamilton actually wrote the subsequent Bessie stories. I'll bet a pound to a penny that he didn't.

1923 – 1942 (Schoolgirls' Own Office Fleetway House/
  Amalgamated Press)   £25 each

Schoolgirls Own Comic

All were published by Amalgamated Press.

No 1 5th February 1921   £20
Other issues to 1936   £4 each

Subsumed into Schoolgirl in 1936

Scottish Football Book

All were published by Stanley Paul and doubly dated.

1955 – 1972   £5 each

Scout

1908 – 1940 (Pearson)	£25 each
1941 – 1952 (Newnes)	£12 each
1954 – 1969 (Dating system now for year following	
– Newnes)	£5 each
1961 (Pathfinder – Thames)	£5
1962 – 1969 (Pathfinder – Purnell)	£5 each
1970/80's (Pathfinder – Purnell)	£4 each

Scramble

All were published by Swan. Gerald Swan's most successful artist was EH Banger – responsible for many of the distinctive album and comic covers - who signed himself Bang.

1949 – 1951	£8 each

See also Funnies, Schoolboys/Girls and Slick Fun

Scramble Comics

All were published by Swan.

No 1 March 1947	£8
Other issues	£3 each

See also Slick Fun

Sexton Blake

Sexton Blake first appeared in The Missing Millionaire by Hal Meredith (actually Harry Blyth) in The Halfpenny Marvel as early as December 1893. He was the working man's Sherlock Holmes; a halfpenny was affordable. All were published in soft covers by Amalgamated Press.

1938 - 1942 in their original boxes	£80 each
1938 – 1942 without boxes	£30 each

Sexton Blake Magazines and Papers

Halfpenny Marvel 13th December 1893	£80
Union Jack May 1984 No 2	£30
Sexton Blake Library 1915 No 1 in First Series	£70
Union Jack renamed Detective Weekly February 1933 No 1	£15

All other issues in the above titles – there were five series of Sexton Blake Library - can be bought for £2 - £3 each

Ships

All were published by Ian Allen.

1958, 1967 – 1969 and 1971   £8 each

Sixer

1960 and 1961 (For all Wolf Cubs – Thames)	£4 each
1963 – 1969 (Purnell)	£4 each
1970/80's (Purnell)	£3 each

Skipper Book for Boys

This book ran as the annual companion to Skipper comic also published by D C Thomson from 1931 – 1947 with some gap years. Priced originally from 2/6 to 5/-, today they change hands for £15 - £20 each.

1932 Two men ride turtles
1933 Ship's captain inspects penguins
1934 Four boys swimming under No Bathing sign
1935 Footballers quiz referee's decision
1936 Chief on rocking horse
1937 Indians watch boy on trolley
1938 Eskimo laughs as man slips on ice into water
1939 Three seamen playing golf with chief
1940 Sailor band plays on beach
1941 Roundabout, tickets, rifles and guns
1942 SS Daisy under bombardment with nonchalant captain
1948 Man, husky and sledge parachuting

Skipper Comic Paper

Skipper was another title in the Big Five published by DC Thomson but it was also the first to fold as wartime paper shortages began to bite and the comics became rationed to fortnightly productions. The annual continued for another two issues albeit 6 years apart.

No 1 6th September 1930   £100
All other issues to 1941   £6 each

Slick Fun

All were published by Swan.

1949 – 1956 (The last two issues had the same covers) £8 each

Slick Fun Comics

All were published by Swan.

No 1 June 1940   £10
Other issues   £3 each

Smash!

Leo Baxendale and Ken Reid previously engaged by DC Thomson were now in full flow for Odhams.

1967 –1970 (Odhams Soft covers)   £5 each
1970's (IPC)   £4 each

See Pow! and Wham!

Smash! Comic

Like the books the comics were published by Odhams and then by IPC. Batman appeared on the cover from Issue No 20.

No 1 5th February 1966   £10
Other issues to 1971   £2 each

Took over Pow! in 1969 and was subsumed into Valiant

Soccer the International Way

All were published by World Distributors.

1968 - 1973   £4 each

Sooty

All were published by The Daily Mirror.

1957 - 1970   £10 each

Space Family Robinson

1966 (Comic Album - World Distributors)   £10
1968 (World Distributors)   £10

Sparkler

All were published by Amalgamated Press and some had covers by Roy Wilson.

1936 - 1940   £15 each

Sparkler Comic

A short run was published by Provincial and the title was later revived by Amalgamated Press. Bertie Brown's Freddie Flip and Uncle Bunkle appeared on the colour front cover from 1935.

No 1 12th September 1931 (Provincial)   £20
Other Provincial issues to 1932   £5 each
No 1 20th October 1934 (Amalgamated Press)   £20
All other issues to 1939   £5 each

Subsumed into Crackers

Sparky Book for Boys and Girls

All were published by DC Thomson.

1968 and 1969   £6 each
1970/80's   £4 each

Sparky Comic

Ali and his Baba were the creation of Malcolm Judge and made their first appearance on 17th January 1977. Published by DC Thomson this comic joined forces with Topper thereafter.

No 1 23rd January 1965	£20
Other issues to July 1977	£1 each

Speed

The DC Thomson publications for 1937 and 1938 are quite scarce. The latter edition has a 30 page unattributed horse racing story.

1934 (Collins)	£6
1937 and 1938 which has man mowing down 4 wolves in ski-car (DC Thomson)	£30 each
1957 (Stories for Boys – Beaver Books)	£5

Sports

1930 and 1931 (Wm Collins)	£10 each
1936 (Book for Boys – Birn Bros)	£10

Stingray

Troy Tempest and Phones do underwater battle with the Aquaphibians.

1966 and 1967 (City Magazines)	£10 each

Storyland (for Girls)

The book was retitled Storyland Annual for Girls after the first issue. All were published by DC Thomson.

1926 Three girls on a stile	£20
1927 Girl and hockey stick	£20
1928 Girl in red and yellow scarf	£20

Summertime Stories

All were published by DC Thomson.

1936 – 1939   £15 each

Sunbeam

All were published by Amalgamated Press.

1933 – 1941   £10 each

Sunbeam Comic

Joe Hardman's Aladdin and His Wonderful Lamp ran for the greater part of the two series from 1928 – 1940 when this Amalgamated Press publication first subsumed Puck and then capitulated to Tiny Tots. There was a war on for Pete's sake!

No 1 7th October 1922   £40
No 1 30th January 1926 (New Series)   £20
All other issues to May 1940   £5 each

Sunny Stories

1955 – 1966 (Newnes)   £8 each
1967 – 1970 (Pearson)   £5 each
1970's (IPC)   £3 each

Sunny Stories Papers

There were two series both published by Newnes. G Higham's little fairy Tina appeared in No 1 of the New Series on 12th July 1958. Harry Banger drew Dilly Duckling from 1952. Enid Blyton was of course the main attraction with Betsy-May.

No 1 19th June 1942   £30
Other issues to 1967   £3 each
Other issues into 1970's (Fleetway then IPC)   £2 each

Super-Cinema

Both were published by Amalgamated Press in dustwrappers.

1953 – 1955   £12 each

Super Detective Library

The comic had no annual counterpart (see Thriller Picture Library and Classics Illustrated) but is a highly collectable series and must be mentioned. These pocket sized editions published by Amalgamated Press/Fleetway ran for 188 issues from 1953 to 1960.

The early issues are scarce and valuable. You can Meet the Saint in No 1 , Ernest Dudley in No 2, Bulldog Drummond in No 3, The Third Man in No 4 and The Saint again in No 5. Dick Barton turned up in No 12 but you had to wait until No 65 to meet Sherlock Holmes in two mystery stories. He quickly reappeared in Nos 74 and 78. Rick Random, Rip Kirby and Blackshirt are collected titles.

Artists of great talent were employed on the series especially Reg Bunn, W Bryce-Hamilton, Frank Giacoia and Ron Turner. Prices vary considerably but Holmes issues are at a premium of £100 each. Expect to pay dearly for The Saint – perhaps £60 each. Other issues would be in the £8 - £15 region.

Super-Thriller

1958 and 1960 (World Distributors)   £6 each

Super Adventure

All pre 1970 titles were published by Atlas using the double dating system.

1958/59	£30
1959/60	£20
1960 – 1969	£10 each
1970's (Top Sellers)	£8 each

Superboy

All were published by Atlas using the double dating system.

1953/54	£40
1954/55	£30
1955 – 1960	£20 each
1961 – 1967	£12 each

Superboy Comics

Superboy covers the years of Clark Kent's adolescence and was first published by DC Comics in the USA in March 1949. A fine example today is worth around £1500. American issues were not available in the UK until imported by Thorpe and Porter in 1959 and they were over stamped with the price of 6d or 9d. The first thus was No 77 which is worth about £30 today. Subsequent issues to No 100 are variously priced between £20 and £40.

Supercar

These Wm Collins publications were Gerry Anderson spin-offs from the Thunderbirds.

1962 and 1963 (Mike Mercury in)	£15 each

Superman

All pre 1969 titles were published by Atlas using the double dating system after the first two issues.

1951 (Bumper Edition)	£100
1952	£60
1953/54	£40
1954 – 1961	£20 each
1961 – 1968	£10 each
1969 – 1970 (Top Sellers)	£6 each
1970/80's	£4 each

Superman Story Book

All were published by World Distributors.

1967 - 1969   £10 each

Superman Comics

In the mid 1930's Jerry Siegel wrote the story of the baby who was sent to earth - interesting how the great stories reflect religious themes - to save him from certain death on his home planet of Krypton. That baby grew into manhood as the meek and gentle Clark Kent. You know the rest of the story or you have been living on a different planet for the last 60 years.

Joe Shuster was impressed and inspired by Siegel's story and set to work on the illustrations. It was five years before they found a publisher having had umpteen rejections. DC Comics published the first ever Superman story in June 1938 in Action Comic No 1. A Fine copy today is worth in the region of £20000.

Superman comics issued in the UK and Australia were published and distributed by Atlas between 1950 and 1962.

No 1 April 1950   £180
Nos 2 - 5   £45 each
Nos 6 - 50   £15 each
Nos 50 - 136   £10 each

Supreme Book for Boys/Children/Girls

1964 (Dean)   £5 each

Swift

1955 - 1960 (E Hulton and Co Ltd) Dustwrappers   £8 each
1961 - 1963 (Longacre)   £6 each

Swift Comic

This sister title to Eagle was first published by E Hulton and then by Longacre.

No 1 20th March 1954 £20
Other issues to 1963 £3 each

Added Zip from 1959 and collapsed into the wings of Eagle in 1963

Take Me

Not a title that would win much favour these days. Both were published by DC Thomson.

1935 Little girl with toys and dolls	£15
1936 Little girl and dog on lead	£15

Tarzan

These books were most significantly published by World Distributors.

1960 (Adventure)	£12
1962, 1970 and 1971	£5 each
1970's (World Distributors)	£5 each
1970's (Brown and Watson)	£3 each

Tarzan Comic

The comics were published under licence to United Features first by Peters for 19 issues 1950 – 1951, then by Westworld as Tarzan the Grand Adventure 1951 – 1953 and finally by the latter company as Tarzan Adventures from 1953 – 1959. The comics from any of the three versions are worth about £7 each.

Teddy Bear

1965 – 1969 (Fleetway)	£4 each
1970/80's (IPC)	£3 each

Teddy Bear Comic

Published first by Fleetway and then by IPC the comic was eventually subsumed into Jack and Jill.

Issues 1973 – 1973	£3 each

Teddy Tail

Charles Folkard's Teddy Tail appeared as a comic strip in The Daily Mail from 1915. In 1992 we exhibited at The British Show in Toronto and freighted out chests full of what we thought would appeal to British expatriates. Amongst the stock were a dozen or more early Teddy Tail Annuals. We didn't sell a single one but decided after the three days of the show to find a local bookshop that would buy them. They wouldn't! How is it that a character so successful for the Daily Mail as to worry the Daily Express into creating Rupert Bear in self-defence is so totally undervalued? In the end we gave them away in Canada rather than pay the freight home.

1934 – 1941 (Wm Collins)	£10 each
1949 – 1962 (Associated Newspapers)	£5 each

Teeney-Weeney

All were published by Epworth Press.

1929 – 1939	£10 each

Television

All were published by Odhams.

1951 – 1961	£6 each

Thriller Picture Library

Edited by the late Leonard Matthews this Amalgamated Press/ Fleetway publication although having no annual counterpart deserves serious attention. The comic attracts a great deal of interest from collectors and early issues are very scarce. Although the covers were specially drawn by William Bryce Hamilton and Geoff Campion the first two stories were reprinted from Amalgamated Press's Knock-Out – a careful beginning to a publisher's new venture. The new comic was so successful however the reprints soon dwindled and new artwork and scripts were commissioned from Philip Mendoza (Gulliver's Travels and Ali Baba) and Geoff Campion (Robin Hood and Last of the Mohicans). There were a total of 450 issues between 1951 and 1963.

No 1 The Three Musketeers	£150
Nos 2 – 10	£60
Nos 11 – 50	£20 each
Nos 51 – 100	£10 each
All other issues	£5 each

Thumper (Walt Disney's)

All were published by Odhams.

| 1952 – 1956 | £12 each |

Thunderbirds

1966 (City Magazines)	£12 each
1967 and 1968 (Century 21)	£10 each
1969 (Captain Scarlet and – Century 21)	£10
1971 (Century 21) and 1972 (Purnell)	£6 each

Tiger

1957 – 1959 (Amalgamated)	£18 each
1960 – 1969 (Fleetway)	£10 each
1970/80's (IPC)	£5 each

Tingha and Tucker

| 1968 and 1971 (World Distributors) | £5 each |

Tiny Tots

1899 – 1926 (Cassells)	£15 each
1928 – 1959 (Revised dating system hence no 1927 – Amalgamated Press)	£6 each
1960 (Fleetway)	£6

Tiny Tots Comic

Amalgamated Press published this extremely successful title which ran for over 30 years. See Playhour, Playbox, Rainbow and Tiger Tim

| No 1 22nd October 1927 | £40 |

Loose Leaf Page

Tiger

See Roy of the Rovers

Tiger Comic

Brian Leigh's British Gladiator Olac showed the Romans how to go on. This was always my favourite comic. I couldn't wait to see what the Melchester team was up to week by week! All were published by Amalgamated Press/Fleetway/IPC.

No 1 11th September 1954	£100
Issues to 1959	£4 each
Issues to 1980	£2 each

The comic variously acquired Comet (1959), Champion and Hurricane (1965) and Jag (1969)

Tiger Tim

Tiger Tim was a giant in the development of British comic culture yet the books in which he featured - and there are many - are seriously undervalued at this time. See Mrs Hippo, Playbox, Playhour and Rainbow. All were published by Amalgamated Press.

1922	£35
1923 - 1957	£15 each

Tiger Tim's Weekly

All were published by Amalgamated Press.

No 1 31st January 1920	£60
All other issues to 1940 (New Series from 1921)	£5 each

Issues to 1959   £4 each

Took over Sunbeam (1940) and Rainbow (1956) before being
subsumed into Playhour in 1959

Tip Top (My)

Cowboys and Indians figured and Happy Bob Harriday and his horse
Rocky were as good as it could get.

1937 – 1948 (Epworth Press)   £10 each
1950 – 1955 (Book – Amalgamated Press)   £5 each

Tip Top Comic

This was another successful Amalgamated Press publication not to
be confused with Ransom reprints or the L Miller US reprints. The
wartime adventures of Brownie the Moorland Pony were especially
anticipated.

No 1 21st April 1934   £20
All other issues to 1954   £4 each

Added Butterfly to title from 1940 and was subsumed by TV Fun in
1954

Toby Twirl

Written by Sheila Hodgetts and illustrated by Edward Jeffrey the
wonderful stories of the little pig with the curly tail were all
published by Sampson, Low, Marston and Co. They were named
variously Toby Twirl Annual/Story Book/Adventure Stories/
Adventures. Books with dustwrappers are worth double listed
prices.

1946 Toby Twirl with treasure and dragon
  behind rocks   £15
1947 Toby with basket, Eli, a giant, a gnome and
  a wooden man   £15
1948 Toby and Eli on horseback with a windmill
  in landscape   £15

1949 Toby, Eli and Pete in a mud pool	£15
1950 Toby flying on a tortoise's back	£15
1951 Toby and Co on a pirate raft	£15
1952 Toby and Co with a helicopter	£15
1953 Toby with the engine Dilly Puff	£15
1954 Dilly Puff with Eli; Toby and cottage pulled by donkey	£15
1955 Toby, Eli, Pete in diving suit and a sailor on deck	£15
1956 Toby and Eli on a paddle boat	£15
1957 Toby, Pete and Eli with a genie	£15

Toby Twirl Books

Sampson Low published a series of dustwrappered titles in smaller format to correspond with the Noddy books of the same period. There were 8 of them each one numbered published between 1949 and 1954.

Nos 1 – 8 in dustwrappers £20 each

There were three titles published in a large card-covered format in the late 40's early 50's. Although we have had all three titles I only have notes about two of them – Toby Twirl in Pogoland and Toby Twirl and the Magic Ring. All three are worth about £70 each as they are much scarcer than Rupert and the Wonderful Boots which emanated from the same publisher in the same format.

There were 5 strip books which are scarcer than their Noddy equivalents £25 each

Other Toby Twirl books of note are:

The Toby Twirl Colour Strip Adventure Book (1953)
The New Toby Twirl Colour Strip Adventure Book (1954)
Toby Twirl on Dapple Heath (1954) £25 each

Toddlers

1928 –1934 (Treasure – John Leng)	£12 each
1968 - 1969 (Own/Own Colour – Fleetway)	£5 each
1970's (IPC)	£3 each

Toddles

1956 and 1957 (Wm Collins)   £5 each

Tom and Jerry

All were published by World Distributors.

1968   £10
1970/80's   £4 each

Tom and Jerry Comic/Weekly

Dell reprinted just 4 issues from USA in 1953   £8 each
The weekly published in UK by Dell ran to 43
   issues from 13th October 1973   £2 each

Tom Browne's

1899 (Comic – Newnes)   £40
1904 and 1905 (Christmas – HJ Drane)   £40 each

Tom Merry

All were published by Mandeville in dustwrappers.

1949 Gus and Tom Merry awakened to find
   Cardew on the floor   £15
1950 A burglar meets a ghost   £15
1951 School shields displayed   £15
1952 Snowball fight   £15
1953 Goal-mouth incident   £15
1954 Ice-skating fellows   £15

See Gem

Tony Blackburn Pop Special

1969 and 1970 (Atlas)   £5 each
1971 (World Distributors)   £5

Top Cat

It always used to amuse me to see the BBC listing this programme as Boss Cat when we could plainly hear Top Cat as the signature tune. Was this a wonderful piece of subliminal advertising by the cat food company?

1963 (Comic Album)	£10
1964 and 1968 (World Distributors)	£8 each
1970's (Pemberton)	£4 each

Top Pop Stars

All were published by Purnell.

1963 – 1971	£6 each
1972 – 1979 (Pop Scene)	£4 each

Topical Times

All were published by DC Thomson.

1927 – 1932 (Football Double dating system)	£15 each
1932 – 1940 (Sporting Doubly dated)	£12 each
1959 – 1966 (Football Doubly dated)	£8 each
1961 (Girls all Sports)	£8
1970/80's (Football Doubly dated)	£4 each

Topper Book

Topper was another great success for publishers DC Thomson with Dudley Watkins' Mickey the Monkey as the star of the production.

1954 An unusually large card covered natural history book	£100
1955 Five strips of characters across front board	£55
1956 Various characters/creatures in dartboard arrangement	£35
1957 Twenty five square pictures of characters and things	£25
1958 As 1957 but diamond shapes	£25
1959 Blue cover with Bungle pointing rifle across page	£20

1960 Diagonal title   £15
1961 Mexican and horse laughing at Topper   £15
1962 Pale blue with characters names under their
      picture   £15
1963 Deck chair and drawing pins gag   £15
1964 Chicken holds up fox – Man bites dog sort of thing! £15
1965 Mexican, cowboy and a firework   £15
1966 Black cover with cat playing with firework   £10
1967 – 1979 are all dated to the front cover   £5 each

Topper Comic

No 1 7th February 1953   £150
Issues to 1969   £4 each
Issues to 1979   £2 each

Tottenham Hotspur

All were published by Stanley Paul.

1968 – 1972   £5 each

Trains

All were published by Ian Allen.

1954 – 1971   £5 each

Treasure

1964 – 1969 (For Boys and Girls - Fleetway)   £4 each
1967 – 1969 (Book of Animals – Fleetway)   £4 each
1970's (Boys and Girls/Book of Animals – IPC) £3 each

Triumph

1937 – 1941 (Amalgamated Press)   £12 each
1937 (For Boys/Children/Girls – Wm Collins)   £8 each

Triumph Comic Paper

Superman no less appeared from 1939 as a strip in Triumph fresh from his 1938 debut in Action Comic. All were published by Amalgamated Press.

No 1 18th October 1924 £50
Issues to 1940 £5 each

Took over Gem in 1940 but succumbed only 4 months later to the charms of Champion

Trumpton (Gordon Murray's)

1968 – 1973 (Purnell) £8 each

TV Century 21

1965 – 1966 (City Magazines) £10 each
1967 - 1969 (Century dropped from title – Century 21) £10 each
1970 – 1973 (IPC) £8 each

TV Comic

This book had more publishers than Big Ron Atkinson had football clubs!

1954 – 1957 (News of the World) £12 each
1958 (Daily Express) £12
1959 – 1961 (Oldbourne) £8 each
1962 – 1968 (TV Publications) £8 each
1969 and 1970 (Argus) £5 each
1971 (Daily Express) £5
1970/80's (Argus) £4 each

TV Comic Comic

Mr Pastry appeared in issue No 1 and stayed for 7 years. The comic published like the annual by The News of The World until 1958 had a long life into the 1980's.

No 1 9th November 1951 £30
Other issues to 1959 £4 each
1960 – 1969 £2 each
All other issues £1 each

Took over TV Express and TV Land (1962), TV Action (1973), Tom and Jerry Weekly (1974) and Target (1978)

TV 21 Comic

Published by City Magazines the comic took over TV Tornado in 1968 and added Joe 90 to its title in 1969.

No 1 6th January 1968   £10
Nos 2 – 90 (1969)   £4 each

TV Fun

All were published by Amalgamated Press.

1958 – 1960   £8 each

TV Fun Comic

George the Jolly Gee-Gee (See Radio Fun) made a return as Hoofer the Tee-Vee Gee-Gee drawn by Roy Wilson for Amalgamated Press.

No 1 19th September 1953   £40
All other issues to September 1959   £3 each

Incorporated Jingles and Tip Top from May 1954 and subsumed by TV Fun in 1959

TV Land

All were published by TV Publications.

1962 – 1965   £6 each

TV Picture Stories

Published by Pearson these small comics are worth a mention in spite of having no annual counterparts. They ran from 1958 – 1960 and included such titles as Dixon of Dock Green, Emergency Ward Ten, and O.S.S.   £7 each

TV Tornado

All were published by World Distributors.

1967 – 1970   £10 each

TV Tornado Comic

The comics were published by City Magazines until being subsumed by TV21 in 1968.

No 1 14th January 1967   £10
Other issues to 1968   £5 each

Uncle Mac

There were two series of Children's Hour Annuals. The first series was published by Hutchinson and is really quite scarce. The book for 1935 was published in a black and white wrapper although the two subsequent issues had coloured wrappers. I have been unable to trace annuals for 1938 to 1943 and imagine they do not exist but I would be happy to be proved wrong. The later books were published by Sampson Low in a smaller format and are relatively common. Derek McCulloch edited all the annuals. He was better known to thousands of children as Uncle Mac.

1935 – 1937   £20 each
1944 – 1947 (Sampson Low) Dustwrappers   £5 each

Valentine

1959 – 1969 (Pop Special - Fleetway)   £6 each
1970/80's   £3 each

Valentine Magazine

No 1 19th January 1957   £20
Issues to 1974   £2 each

Expect to pay at least double for Beatles and Elvis features

Valiant

1964 - 1969 (Fleetway)	£8 each
1970/80's (IPC)	£4 each

Valiant Comic

No 1 6th October 1962	£20
All issues to 1976	£2 each

The comic took over Knockout (1963), Smash! (1971), TV21 (1971), Lion (1974) and Vulcan (1976) but lost out to Battle in 1976. A case of winning the war and losing to Battle.

Victor

All were published by DC Thomson.

1964 Commandos at St Nazaire	£15
1965 Commandos at Singapore	£15
1966 – 1969 All dated	£10 each
1970/80's	£5 each

Victor Comic

Alf Tupper was about the best. In 1962 this apprenticed welder/athlete was drawn by Peter Sutherland having been rescued from the 1949 Rover where he had been the Tough of the Track for DC Thomson publications.

No 1 25th February 1961	£35
Issues to 1969	£3 each
1970/80's (Wizard, Hotspur, Scoop and Buddy taken on board)	£1 each

Voyage to the Bottom of the Sea

1965 and 1966 (World Distributors)	£8 each

Wagon Train

1960 – 1961 (Daily Mirror)	£8 each

1960, 1962 and 1963 (World Distributors)   £10 each
1961 (Comic Album – World Distributors)   £10

Walt Disney

1938 (Happy Annual Wm Collins)   £150
1938 (Silly Symphony Wm Collins)   £150
1939 (Snow White and Magic Mirror 3D – Dean)   £60
1939 (Snow White and Seven Dwarfs – Collins)   £90
1963 – 1965 (Toyland- Purnell)   £12 each

See Donald Duck, Mickey Mouse and Thumper

Walt Disney Series

A lovely series published by World Distributors in USA were reprinted in colour by Dell from 1952 in UK.
    There were 52 issues   £8 each

Wee Folks

1902 – 1903 (Nister)   £30 each

West Ham United Football Book

1969 – 1971 (Stanley Paul)   £4 each

Western

1946 – 1947 (Album – Swan)   £8 each
1951 – 1962 (Film – MacDonald) Issued in dustwrappers £10 each
1953 – 1956 (Fun Album – Swan)   £8 each
1955 – 1958 (Round Up – World Distributors)   £10 each
1961 (Round Up Comic – World Distributors)   £12
1964 (Film and TV- Purnell)

Wham!

1966 – 1971 (Odhams)   £6 each
1972 – 1974 (Pow added to title in 1973 – IPC)   £6 each

Wham! Comic

Wham! Comics and Annuals are my best guess as to an investment area for the future. Odhams Press already had Leo Baxendale who had drawn Little Plum and Bash Street Kids for DC Thomson and they now recruited Ken Reid who had drawn Roger the Dodger and Jonah for the same publication. This formidable duo were unleashed on Wham! Leo Baxendale drew Biff, Danny Dare, Footsie the Clown, General Nitt, Pest of the West, The Tiddlers, Georgie's Germs and Eagle Eye. Ken Reid had Frankie Stein and Jasper the Grasper among others.

No 1 20th June 1964 £15
All other issues to 1968 £2 each

Subsumed by Pow! 1968

Whiskers

The strips were drawn by Gwynne (Cyril Price) of the Daily Graphic and republished in coloured form in the annuals.

1948 – 1952 (Kemsley Newspapers/Daily Graphic) £10 each

Whizzbang Comic

1942 and 1943 (Amalgamated Press) £12 each

Wild West

1953 – 1960 (Comic – World Distributors) £10 each
1954 (Book – Birn Bros) £8

Wilfred

1924 – 1939 (Daily Mirror) £20 each

See Pip and Squeak

Willie Waddle

They were published by John Leng of Dundee and today are worth

£12 each. I am not aware of any issues other than these listed.

1928 Ducklings given a blackboard lesson watched by animals over red fence
1929 Willie amuses crowd by imitating unamused peacock with feather duster tail
1930 Willie and pig slide into duck pond
1931 Willie holds up charabanc party on his little bike
1932 Smiling Willie sits behind umbrella to defend himself from snowballs
1933 Willie checks himself in the mirror on the way to a party
1934 Willie and gang camping and preparing breakfast
1935 Willie sings with gusto on stage
1936 Willie on station platform take a trolley ride
1937 Willie is lassooed by dog in western outfit
1938 Willie in flight accompanied by eagle who'd probably like to eat him
1939 Willie as a pavement artist
1940 Willie sails on the local pond in a tin bath with red sail
1946 Willie and ducklings on a sledge
1947 Willie speeds across the beach in his sail car
1948 Willie on top of a charabanc

Wizard

All were published by DC Thomson.

1936 Crowded camping scene – note the bull	£25
1937 Crowded sporting event	£20
1938 Crowded snow scene	£20
1939 Crowded camping scene – note the dog and the donkey	£20
1940 Canadian mountie chases his man across the ice	£20
1941 Pirates attempt to take over the ship from gallant cabin boy	£20
1942 Man tracking edge of waterfall bearing a canoe	£20
1949 Wall of death cyclist with leopard passenger	£10

Wizard Comic Paper

Whenever the subject of Wizard – another of the DC Thomson Big Five – is brought up there is one character who stands out in memories above all others – Wilson. William Wilson did not appear in the comic until 1943 but he made such an impact that he stayed until 1980 though finishing his career in Hotspur after a twelve year sojourn at Hornet. But what would you expect of a man who could run a mile in 3 minutes 48 seconds long before Roger Bannister even thought of it? Not bad for a man well over a hundred years old living on a diet of berries – Wilson not Bannister. This important comic was published by DC Thomson.

No 1 23rd September 1922	£200
Issues 1922 – 1939	£8 each
Issues 1940 –1949	£5 each
Issues 1950 – 1963	£3 each

The comic was revived in 1970 for a further 400 plus issues incorporating Rover from 1973 before capitulating to Victor in 1978.

Wizard Holiday Book

Both were published by DC Thomson. We have only ever had these wonderful paper-covered books in stock once and would love to see those detailed Chick Gordon covers again.

1938 Crowded beach scene	£150
1939 Crowded cable car scene	£150

Wolf Cub

These books were published mostly by Pearson although Newnes published a couple of the War years.

1938 – 1952	£8 each
1954 – 1967 New dating system left out 1953	£5 each

Wonder Book

1904 – 1928 Ward Lock and Co was added to the title after the first issue. Many, many titles were published by Ward Lock all having one thing in common – a complete lack of serious commercial value. The sepia and bottle green glossy plates appeared rather flat in spite of the efforts of quality illustrators like Harry Theaker, Warwick Goble, Rowland Wheelwright – she also illustrated Tristram Shandy - and Margaret Tarrant. Thomas Maybank of Oojah fame was also involved. Today you could expect to pick them up for about £10 each.

Wonderland for Boys and Girls

1921 – 1926 (Amalgamated Press) £8 each

World's Best Boys

1926 – 1937 (Allied Newspapers) £6 each

Wuff, Snuff and Tuff

1949 – 1951 (Odhams) £8 each

Yogi Bear

1964 –68 (Hanna-Barbera - World Distributors)	£8 each
1969 (Hanna-Barbera Atlas)	£8
1970/80's	£4 each
1962 – 1965 (Comic Annual - World Distributors)	£8 each

Yogi Bear's Own Weekly

The comic was published by City Magazines.

No 1 27th October 1962	£10
Nos 2 – 76 (1964)	£4 each

Subsumed by Huckleberry Hound in 1964

Young Airman's

1941 (Wm Collins) £15

Young England

1880 – 1937 (Melrose/Pilgrim Press/Sunday School Union) £8 each

Young People

See Harper's

Z Cars

1964 – 1967 (World Distributors)   £6 each

Zip

1959 and 1960 (Dean)   £5 each

Zip Comic

All were published by Odhams.

No 1 4th January 1958   £15
Nos 2 – 92   £4 each

Subsumed by Swift in 1959

Zoom

1941 (DC Thomson) RAF bomber releasing bombs
  into sea   £25

Zorro

These two books were published by The Daily Mirror in
dustwrappers.

1958 and 1959   £10 each

Zorro Comics

Miller reprinted 38 issues after National Publications
  1952 – 54   £6 each
Dell reprinted 6 issues after World Distributors
  in 1955   £6 each

A Look into The Crystal Ball
Annuals first issued in the 1970's

I supply the date of the first annual of a series but have generally ignored books which only ran to one issue. I have also included a couple of 1980 titles that have some promise for the future.

As yet most of these books have little commercial value so you should be able to pick them up for a fiver or less.

My best guess as to what will be the collectable Rupert and Beano books of tomorrow would undoubtedly be the collectable Rupert and Beano books of today.

However I have produced a star rating system on the following list. The more stars the more I rate the chances of success.

Wealth Warning
Remember the value of books can go down as well as up and you may not retrieve the amount you have invested.

Abba 1979 ***
Action 1977
Action Man 1978
Aeronauts 1973
Alan Ball's International Soccer 1970
Ali Cat 1978
Alias Smith and Jones 1976
Angels 1977
Arsenal Football 1970 **
Asterix 1980*
Avengers 1975 *
Bagpuss 1975
Barbapapa 1976
Basil Brush 1971
Battle Picture Weekly 1976 *
Bay City Rollers 1976 **
BBC Grandstand 1979
Beep Beep Road Runner 1974
Bionic Woman 1978
Black Beauty 1976
Blue Jeans 1979
Bobo Bunny 1971

Bod 1977 *
Buses 1971
Catweazle 1971
Charlie's Angels 1978 *
Chart Toppers 1979
Cheeky 1979
Chelsea Football 1971 **
Chigly 1970
Clangers 1971
Cor 1972 **
Countdown 1972
Crackerjack 1970
Dad's Army 1974
Dalek, Terry Nation's 1974
Daredevil 1977
David Essex 1976
Disco 1976
Disneyland 1972
Donald and Mickey 1973
Dougal 1971 ***
Famous Five 1978*
Fantastic Four 1971
Flowerpot Men/Woodentops 1971 *

Flumps 1978
Follyfoot 1974
Funky Phantom 1976
Goal 1975
Great Grape Ape 1978
Happy Days 1979 *
Hazell 1979
Hector's House 1970 *
Hey Diddle Diddle 1973
High Chaparral 1970
Horse and Pony 1977
Horse World 1970
Incredible Hulk 1978 *
Jackie 1975
Jag
Jamie/Magic Torch 1979
Jinty 1975
Just William 1978*
Kevin Keegan's Soccer 1977
Knockout 1973
Kojak 1977 **
Krazy 1978
Kung Fu 1976**
Land of the Giants 1971
Laurel and Hardy 1970 **
Little Star 1974
Logan's Run 1979 *
Look-In TV 1972
Magpie 1970
Man City Football 1970 **
Mandy 1971
Mary Mungo Midge 1971 *
Match of the Day 1979
Matchbox 1980 *
Mates 1976
Mr Benn 1972
Mr Men 1980 **
Misty 1979
Monster Fun 1977
Mork and Mindy 1980 **
Motor Racing International 1971
Multi-Coloured Swap Shop 1979
Muppet Show 1978 **
Music Star 1974

My Fairyland 1970
My First 1971
My Guy 1979
My Very Own 1970
New Musical Express 1973 *
New Scout 1977
New Superman 1979
News of World (Football) 1970
Nursery (Playtime/Rhyme) 1971
Oh Boy! 1978
Once Upon a Time 1970
Osmonds 1976
Parsley 1971
Partridge Family 1974
Pelliphant 1973
Persuaders 1973 *
Peter Fairley's 1971
Photoplay Film 1971
Pink 1974
Pink Panther 1974 **
Planet of the Apes 1977
Playgroup 1978
Playing for Celtic 1970 *
Playing for Rangers 1970 *
Playschool 1971
Pop Group 1977
Popswop 1974
Professionals 1978 *
Puffin 1975
Purnell's Science 1977
Railway World 1972
Record Mirror 1976
Riding 1976
Rod Hull and Emu 1978
Rod Stewart 1978 *
Rolf Harris 1970
Roobarb 1976
RSBP Bird Life 1977
Sally 1971
Sammy the Shunter 1977
Sandie 1973
Scooby Doo 1976 *
Scorcher 1971
Score ('n' Roar) 1972

Scouting 1971
Secret Seven 1979 *
Sesame Street 1979
Shiver and Shake 1974 *
Shoot 1971
Sindy 1971
Sir Prancelot 1973
Six Million Dollar Man 1977 ***
Skippy 1970 *
Smurfs 1980 *
Soccer Super Stars 1977
Space 1999 1976
Spiderman 1975
Star Trek 1970 ***
Star Wars 1979 **
Starsky and Hutch 1978 *
Striker 1971
Sun for Boys/Girls 1974
Sun Soccer 1972
Super TV Heroes 1976
Supersonic 1977
Superstars 1977
Sweeney 1977
Tammy 1972
Television Cartoon 1977
TV Chimps 1977

Tell Me Why 1970
Things to Make and Do 1972
Thomas the Tank Engine 1979 **
Thunder 1972
Timbuctoo 1979
Titans 1977
Toby 1977
Top of the Pops 1974
Toytown 1973
Twinkle 1970
2000AD 1978 **
Wacky Races 1971*
Walt Disney's Now I Know 1974
War Picture Library 1976 *
Warlord for Boys 1977 *
Watch with Mother 1976
Whizzer and Chips 1971 **
Whoopee! 1975
Willy the Kid 1976 ***
Wombles 1974 **
Wonderful World of Disney 1977 *
World of (Purnell Series) 1971
(Angling/Cricket/Football/Golf/
Horse Racing and Motor Sport etc)
World of Sport 1979
Young Master Mind 1978

NOTES

NOTES